Dancing on the Edge

For Jessica +Russ
In the Spirit of the Canyon

Charly Heavenrich

Dancing on the Edge

—

A Grand Canyon Adventure

CHARLY HEAVENRICH

For information, contact:
Charly Heavenrich
Beyond the Edge Publishing
P.O. Box 1555
Boulder, CO 80306-1555
(303) 545-5414
cheavnrich@aol.com
www.Heavenrich.com

ISBN: 0-9667990-0-3

Library of Congress Catalog Card Number: 98-96723

Second Edition

"A Rare Find" by Randall Rieman is printed with permission of the
poet. It was originally published in the book *New Cowboy Poetry: A
Contemporary Gathering*.

Book and cover design by Paulette Livers Lambert

What Readers Are Saying About Dancing on the Edge

I've just finished the book. I can't tell you how much I loved it, so many lessons, things to think about, things that just ARE Powerful stuff Charly Heavenrich. Your book was just what I needed, reminded me of my truth, nudged me back in the direction I've sort of wandered off of

> Barbara, Artist
> Washington State

I got home yesterday from a Grand Canyon trip. While on this trip two people in our group read your book and had great experiences with it. One person felt it was changing his life.

> Joe, Potter
> Utah

I've recommended Charly's book to all my friends. Everyone loves it. Most of my friends who have read it have gone on to make wonderful changes in their lives, it's like they were poised on the brink of making a decision, and when they read his book, it helped guide them. Even my boss at the clinic, our clinic manager - she read it and gave her notice!

> Linda, Social Worker
> Kentucky

I have talked this book up to everyone I know. It literally helped me make the choices I made that changed my life so dramatically. I keep it handy too for reference. I have so many parts of the book highlighted, and/or dog-eared, I can pick up the book anytime and find the inspiration I need for that moment in time.

> Fran, Health Care Worker
> Tennessee

I have just reached chapter 11 of your book. It has been mesmerizing. Spirit Dancer is speaking to me also. I want you to know what a fabulous book this is. It must be making quite an impact on all who read it. Congratulations to you for having the courage to put this experience into words for the rest of us to share.

> Kathy, Raft Passenger
> Georgia

Sitting down to write this note to you is rather difficult...only because it means pulling myself away from your book, *Dancing on the Edge*, that I just purchased today. But I feel compelled to do so NOW, because the inspiration to express my appreciation is so strong.

> Sharanna, In Transition
> Colorado

As a "travelogue," it was very fascinating and interesting – I could not put it down. But, more significantly, your book has really touched some chords in me and is helping me to look at some things in my life differently. Your book provides me with some additional tools, some new ways to look at things. Your candid expression about your journey, your confusion and fears, and your decision to make some major life changes fills me with hope and a sense of empowerment. Your book reminds me that, even though I haven't discovered my answers yet, I know they're in me – if I keep working at it, I will find them.

> Laura, Executive
> Colorado

I received a great X-Mas gift this year... a copy of *Dancing on the Edge*. You have absolutely no idea how close to home it hit. I loved it and think that I have probably read it or portions of it at least 3 times since I received it. Not only did it remind me of the physical beauty of the canyon and the exhilaration of riding the waves, but it also put into words a lot of things that I have been thinking over the past two or three years.

> Scott, Student
> Wisconsin

I'm sad to say I've reached the end of the book, but happy to be at the beginning of my life. It has reached deep into my being and I am moved beyond what I can express. What a wonderful experience to share in your adventure through the Canyon, while learning so much along the way. Your fine writing talent created such a rich experience...I felt that I was right there

Sharon, Photographer
Colorado

Your book was FABULOUS. I can't tell you how much it impacted me. I read it all in two (long) nights. Couldn't put the book down.

Louise, Consultant
Connecticut

It was wonderful to read. I felt as though you and I were having the same first experience, you described it just as I recall I felt on my first trip. It was so delicious to visit those feelings again.

Suzanne, Consultant
Idaho

I've finished reading your book, *Dancing on the Edge*. It is the first one I have read where I don't get lost in the jargon. Many thanks for that. I lent your book to a friend at the gym. She says, like me, that she can really feel the special qualities of the canyon through your writing.

Gillian, Housewife
Australia

I was enthralled by *Dancing on the Edge*. Charly managed to combine gripping descriptions of exciting experiences and magnificent scenery with deep and meaningful insights into the human spirit. I do not read "inspirational" books. I find most of them shallow and dull. This one not only inspired, it enchanted. I will read it again and again.

Jo, Retired
North Carolina

I purposely took a long time to read *Dancing on the Edge*. Partly because I didn't want to leave this wonderful, serene place and partly because I wanted to enjoy and digest every savory bite. I've underlined SO MUCH and I will keep this book close by to help remind me of its many fantastic life lessons. Charly, thank you for sharing your gift with us.

Tina, Housewife
England

Most of us would think of trekking through the Grand Canyon to be an outer journey. Charly brings it one step further by exploring the Canyon as an outer *and* inner journey. Be prepared for the unavoidable inspiration to experience the Canyon for yourself after reading this book!

Scott, Social Worker
Colorado

The author has a compelling style that makes you feel part of his journey. I am richer in the spirit because of you, Charly Heavenrich!

Kathie, Consultant
Michigan

Once I opened the cover and began reading your book, a sense of peace filled my heart. I began to be able to replace most of my 'whys' with 'why nots' as I turned each page. I read your book three times - a few chapters at a time twice, the third time reviewing and highlighting what was most helpful and applicable to me. Six weeks after I received *Dancing on the Edge*, I was at a late summer grill out on a private lake. At that evening get-together, I was approached about interviewing for a different job, and I found a cottage that looked as though it could fit 'me.' At the end of another six weeks, I had a new job and a new home. I had found the courage to set the past to rest and continue on a healthier journey. By stepping back, looking at 'the wheel,' and seeing my own life from the different perspectives, my dream became a reality.

Linda, Health Care Worker
Tennessee

To Annie and Wally, for letting me go to my edges

Acknowledgments

I send my gratitude to all who have supported me on my adventures in life and in the Canyon. Without my friends and family I would not have persevered. Without Wilderness World and Canyon Explorations, the concessionaires who employ me, I would not have come to know this remarkable natural wonder. For this I feel blessed and grateful. Eternal thanks to Gary Casey for inviting me on my first Canyon trip and then helping me continue to return. I can't say enough about my teachers who have helped me recognize my gifts. Special thanks to Swiftdeer for his outrageous teachings which have led to a stronger connection with myself, with others, with the natural world, and with Spirit. Finally, I would like to send my appreciation to all who courageously and passionately share the lessons of the natural world through outdoor adventure programs. You are an amazing group of men and women, and I am fortunate to work with you.

"A Rare Find" by Randall Rieman is printed with permission of the poet. It is a remarkable expression of one of the many gifts people receive during a raft trip in the Grand Canyon, the gift of friendship through shared experience. Mr. Rieman is allowing his poem to be reprinted with the understanding that he does not endorse some of the ideas presented in this book, as they are contrary to his spiritual convictions.

Thanks to Stuart Cowan, author of *Ecological Design*, for his editing; Phyllis Cronbaugh for her enthusiastic support; and Paulette Livers Lambert for her creativity in designing the book's cover and interior.

Life is an adventure. It's like going on a raft trip in the Grand Canyon. You have a choice about going on the journey, and you can't avoid the rapids along the way. Take this journey with me and be inspired to go on your own adventure.

—Charly Heavenrich

Contents

Foreword

Charly Heavenrich is a unique personality. If you'd never seen Charly, but knew he had a Bachelors Degree in History and a Masters Degree in Business and International Finance, you might imagine an extremely serious individual wearing an Armani business suit, sitting behind a big mahogany desk on Wall Street. But, when you discovered he was also an aerobics instructor having had his own television exercise show for three years, you might start wondering if the mahogany desk fit the scene. When you discovered he is a Life Member of the Grand Canyon River Guides' Association, and has been helping individuals explore and interpret the remotest parts of the Canyon since 1978, you might start questioning the Armani suit. Upon learning that Charly is also a dynamic national speaker, having mesmerized audiences for over twenty years with his Grand Canyon metaphors paralleling relevant business and personal challenges, you may see him in another light, a spotlight. Now allow your mental image to reflect an extremely energetic, physically fit individual wearing a brilliant, open-collar, flamboyantly wild, multi-colored shirt, sharing his passion for what may be nature's most awesome creation—the Grand Canyon—and you will have a fairly accurate picture of Charly. His mind is quick and witty, his eyes twinkle and his smile is infectious.

Charly will tell you that he met the Canyon in 1978 and he knew he'd never be the same. Drawn to explore by his own appetite for adventure, he was struck by the magnificent natural beauty, delicate serenity, and sometimes harsh realities of the Grand Canyon.

He quickly recognized the Canyon experience paralleled our own life challenges. Much of our journey is predictable, but to survive and succeed we must be prepared for the unexpected.

After knowing Charly for several years, I had the opportunity to read *Dancing on the Edge,* and was amazed to find that he has another talent. He is also an excellent writer. One of Charly's favorite sayings is, "Life is like going on a Grand Canyon raft trip, you have a choice about going on the journey, but you can't avoid the rapids along the way." *Dancing on the Edge* will take you on a vicarious journey exploring both the depths of who you are, and the depths of the Colorado River snaking deeply through the Grand Canyon. Stand with Charly peering over the edge of the Canyon rim and find your stomach rising to your throat. Fight the panic when you hear the freight-train roar and challenge the twenty-five foot high fifth wave of Hermit rapid with only a small raft and two oars. Relax and float lazily appreciating the beauty of vermilion cliffs, while you expand your knowledge of ancient ruins once inhabited by people who laughed and loved just like you. Discover the lessons taught by Spirit Dancer that changed Charly's life, and may give you insight and motivation to change yours as well. Take the journey and experience the same excitement that coursed through Charly on his first expedition. . . . And, you don't even have to get wet.

—*Phyllis Cronbaugh*
President, Strategic Decisions Plus, Inc.
Member National Speakers Association

Introduction

The Grand Canyon represents a great paradox: powerful, yet peaceful. It is a harsh desert wilderness, but amazingly kind to those who venture through it. Air temperatures that can reach 120 degrees and water as cold as 45 degrees contrast with each other, allowing, even in the wilderness, remarkable comfort for those who visit. Rafting on the Colorado River, snaking through the bottom recesses of the Canyon, brings more paradox. The intensity of the powerful rapids is tempered by serene stretches of water which lull rafters into a false sense of security.

The muted pastels of the Canyon walls at midday complement the brilliant splash of reds, oranges, and golds that paint the rock early and late in the day. As if the sun disdains any competition to its own dazzling display, it drains the rocks of their brilliance, only to slowly relent and return the spectacle of color with its own dying light at the end of the day.

In the Canyon's transforming arms, people experience the difference between what is natural and what has become normal in their lives. A metaphor for life, it provides us with fresh perspectives on our day-to-day adventures and challenges. The Canyon is a teacher, and I'm one of its eager students.

In 1978, I left Detroit for what I assumed was a two week white water rafting vacation in the Grand Canyon. My roommate, a professional raft guide, invited me to be his guest. It was a chance I couldn't pass up, although it wasn't the best time for me to leave my "normal" life. At the time I co-owned a general construction company in southeastern Michigan. We were entering a region-wide slow down in our industry that would eventually result in closing our business.

When I arrived in Flagstaff, Arizona, I learned I would be part of the rafting crew, which meant working harder than I'd ever imagined. First, we assembled and loaded the supplies needed for seventeen passengers on a twelve day trip. I rode on top of the gear piled in back of a two and a half ton stake truck. We called it "Blue" after its sky-blue paint job. With childlike anticipation, I looked down the long ribbon of desert highway gleefully fighting the hot desert winds as we traveled at sixty miles an hour. I'll always remember the exhilaration of that 147 mile trip to Lee's Ferry, nestled on the Colorado River in Northern Arizona.

I'd taken two previous raft trips on the Colorado River in Utah, and I expected my Grand Canyon trip to be much like them: enjoyable, but not life changing. In fact, this trip would be a homecoming, dramatically changing the course—and focus—of my life.

The shift in my perception of the trip started the first morning when, after sleeping on one of the rafts, I opened my eyes and was treated to a spectacular vision. Downstream, the Vermilion Cliffs, named for their majestic horizontal colors, lay reflected on the glassy-calm Colorado River. The sedimentary rock layers, bathed in the alternating reds, golds and oranges of early morning light, delighted me with a work of art unparalleled by any human creation.

After our passengers arrived and selected their rafts for the day, we shoved off from shore and began our journey into the unknown. What happened next can only be described as a homecoming. It became crystal clear I was embarking on much more than a two-week vacation. We hadn't even come to the first rapid, and I already knew my life would be irrevocably changed.

Each day, I grew more captivated by the Canyon itself and the effect it was having on me. Before the end of the trip, I resolved to do whatever it might take to keep coming back to this natural wonder. Today, I am blessed with opportunities to revisit the Canyon as a guide to others, and it never stops being my teacher.

The passengers I take through the Canyon are also my teachers. These people, just like you and me, can be called modern-day explorers who have discovered many truths about the Canyon that relate to life.

- *The quality of the experience—any experience—is up to us.*
- *Much of the journey is predictable, but we must be prepared for the unexpected.*
- *Rapids and change will be encountered along the way.*
- *Eventually we will all come face to face with our limitations—that can be good news.*
- *Success depends upon our relationships with others, as well as on how motivated we are to succeed.*

More than anything, I've discovered how the Grand Canyon supports us in overcoming those self-imposed limitations that are the companions of fear. Many of us fear heights, or the rapids, or failure, or even success, or expressing ourselves fully and passionately in the world. The Canyon shows us the role fear plays in blocking trust in ourselves—and others.

The Grand Canyon is more than a metaphor for life. It's bigger than life, too. In a natural world without pretenses, people create opportunities to explore who they are. While not always comfortable, these experiences always provide us with new awareness.

By shedding the norms of everyday existence, we discover fresh perspectives and awaken to more of who we are and what we can do. All who journey through the Canyon are surprised. Many say their lives are changed, much as was mine. For some, the changes come dramatically and swiftly, while others need time to reflect and integrate the experience into their lives.

David Brower, Dean of US Environmentalists and former Executive Director of the Sierra Club, once quoted a friend who said, "What we should do is put the *Bible* on the shelf for the next twenty years and read the earth." Brower replied, "And if you want a good read, read the Grand Canyon."

The Grand Canyon has taught me we are all explorers seeking to discover secrets that will lead to personal and professional fulfillment. The Canyon experience is a metaphor for life, always providing us with new possibilities as we explore our day-to-day adventures and challenges.

As you read this book, you'll come to see how the Canyon experience offers opportunities for people to deepen their relationships — with themselves, with others, with the natural world, and, for those who are open, with God, or Spirit, or whatever you choose to call a Higher Power. It is a place where people develop fresh perspectives, and new awareness about what is possible. In 1500 AD, Leonardo da Vinci offered this advice:

> *"Every now and then go away, have a little relaxation . . . since to remain constantly at work will cause you to lose power of judgment . . . go some distance away . . . because a lack of harmony or proportion is more readily seen."*

Travel with these modern explorers now. Listen to their stories. Ponder the teachings of Spirit Dancer. Ask yourself, "What does this teach me about me?" Awaken to your Self in this magical adventure through the Grand Canyon. Enjoy the journey.

—Charly Heavenrich
P.O. Box 1555
Boulder, CO 80306
(303) 545-5414
cheavnrich@aol.com
www.heavenrich.com

Chapter One

Spirit Dancer
and the
Puzzle Theory

At 3:00 a.m., a noise outside my window startled me out of a dream. After calming my heart, I lay awake trying to remember the unusual images. I saw a woman in a white robe. I couldn't describe her, but I had a strong feeling she was very important. She had said something to me, but all I could recall were the words "freedom" and "edge". I didn't know what to make of it.

On several occasions over the next few weeks, I felt the dream had returned, but each morning I would wake to a blank chalkboard. I was frustrated. A friend recommended that I leave a notepad and pen by my bed to capture the dream. Still nothing.

One day while hiking in the woods, I remembered that as a young child, I would often talk in my sleep. Maybe I was talking during these dreams. Perhaps I would remember something if I recorded myself during my sleep. I went out and purchased a cheap voice activated tape recorder. I was so excited when I went to bed that night it took me quite some time to fall asleep.

When I awoke in the morning I quickly reached for the recorder near my head and turned it on. Nothing, except for the sounds of bed sheets rustling as I restlessly turned in my sleep. For several weeks I would awaken with no memory of any dream, and only grunts and sighs on the tape recorder. I was becoming discouraged, feeling stupid for what now seemed like a futile quest.

Then one morning the recorder talked. It was like a Haiku poem:

"It happened, once or twice,
that the hat remained on,
while the wearer of the hat,
remained off."

I wondered whether it had any connection to the words in my dream. The answer wasn't long in coming. On an early August night, my dream vividly returned, and in the morning I remembered more than I had before. Again, there was the woman in white, and this time her words were, "The way to freedom is through the danger. Step up to the edge."

Weird. There were those words again, "freedom" and "edge". How could danger lead to freedom? And, what or where was the edge? It made no sense. Then I recalled the poem from my previous dream. Was I the wearer of the hat? Maybe I was the one who was off most of the time?

Already in my mid-thirties I had no clue who I really was and what I wanted out of life. I had a masters degree in finance and my own business, which allowed me to pay the bills, barely. I was active, attractive, according to my friends, and healthy, but couldn't sustain a relationship. There was no meaning in my life, no sense of purpose. Just getting up and making it through the day. This wasn't the way it was supposed to be. My upbringing dictated that by now I should have a wife and kids, and be creating a sizable nest egg for our golden years. Instead I had no money in the bank, no relationship, and a whole lot of dissatisfaction.

In fact, the only thing of value at that time seemed to be the dream. Thank God for the dream. It probably helped me hold on to my sanity. I didn't understand it, but somehow I knew it held secrets that could change my life. The key seemed to be the woman. Who was she? Why had she appeared to me? What did her words mean? I had no answers, only questions.

While browsing in a bookstore a few days later, my attention was drawn to the Native American section and some books about medicine women. As I stood there, my thoughts returned to the past. In my late twenties, I had dated a woman with Chippewa Indian blood. When her great grandmother and great grandfather left their tribe, they made their children swear they would never reveal their Indian identity. Evidently they felt it would be better for them to be raised as whites.

My friend, Benashé, had kept her great grandmother's secret until one day in a history class during her junior year in high school, when she accidentally let it slip. After some initial fear, but no apparent repercussions, she began to explore her roots. Instead of wanting to hide her heritage, she became very proud of it. Several years later, she even started going into schools and sharing her new found tradition with others. It was from her that I'd learned about medicine women.

During the two years we'd dated, I'd become fascinated with various American Indian traditions. I'd also attended several workshops put on by Red Hawk, a Shaman offering the teachings of the medicine wheel and many Native American ceremonies and lessons.

I studied the cover of one book about medicine women, and began wondering why I had quit the studies. I had found it fascinating and I think I would have continued, but Benashé took a job overseas, and we gradually lost touch. For some reason I stopped attending Red Hawk's classes.

As I perused the back cover of the book, the thought crossed my mind, "Was the woman in my dream a medicine woman?" I felt compelled to purchase the book.

That night as I read in bed, I had a flash of recognition. She must be a medicine woman! What I thought was a white robe was actually a white deerskin garment. At that instant I could suddenly see her very clearly. I bolted upright in bed. She appeared as a holographic image in the room with me. Was she real? Her long hair was jet black with streaks of white. Her eyes were very clear and alive, conveying both compassion and wisdom.

Then she spoke with a calm confidence. "My name is Spirit Dancer, and I am sent to guide you on the next part of your journey. You have heard the words I have whispered in your dream time. Now I offer you the chance to gain your freedom."

She paused as if waiting for my answer. I looked around wondering if she was talking to me. Maybe there was someone else in the room. Actually, I was wondering if I'd gone crazy. Could I touch her? Was I hallucinating? Maybe I had gone off the deep end.

The soft voice continued and grabbed my attention. "If you wish to gain your freedom, you must uncover what many humans have forgotten. You have learned to 'play it safe,' giving away your power to choose. You have stopped taking risks and you have stopped growing. Freedom means knowing and living your inner truth." As she talked I noticed that she wore a necklace of garnets with a silver shield in the middle. On the shield, an engraved eagle sat on two lightning bolts, one dark and one light, forming a 'V.' Nine copper feathers hung from the shield, and a brilliant fire opal stared out at me from where the eagle's heart would beat.

"Who are you? Am I dreaming?" I asked. She smiled, ignoring my comments and continued.

"True freedom involves being who you are, taking full responsibility for your choices and your outcomes. I can help you gain that freedom. But I must warn you, if you take on this challenge, you will be embarking on a road which is long and hard. The hardest journey you have ever taken. It will involve great challenges, making mistakes, and learning from them. You will experience many difficulties, doubt, and fear. You may find yourself dancing on the edge quite often. Yet if you are committed and follow through, the rewards will be beyond your imaginings. Are you willing to walk this road?"

My thoughts moved from whether she was real or not, to how badly I wanted a change in my life. She was offering me a gift. I hesitated, remembering the words of Red Hawk during a seminar. He had said, "With a thousand apprentices, I will be lucky to find one who will do what it takes." I doubted myself. Did I have what it would take? I was being drawn to it. However naïve or innocent I was about the process, I wanted my life to be different, much different. There was nothing in my so-called "normal" world that seemed to offer any hope for the changes I longed for.

"Yes, I'm willing." They were my words, but they startled me. That much said, I blurted out the rest. "I can't continue living this way. What do you mean by freedom? What does danger have to do with it? Where is this edge? How will I know when I'm there? Will it be safe?"

Spirit Dancer held up a hand, a serious look on her face. The beautiful white deerskin robe swayed. "Patience. Your journey will begin slowly, for it takes time to wake up. You will need a total commitment and it will require much work. You will become frustrated at times. But know this. As you begin to awaken to who you really are, your world will change, and what you call 'work' will become a wonderful adventure. So start by just being willing. In that willingness you will find your source of strength and the awareness you need to answer these and many other questions. Once again, are you willing?"

"Yes, I want it very much." I answered, almost afraid that if I didn't speak quickly, the gift might be taken away.

"Good." she continued, "Let's begin with two teachings to provide understanding for your journey. My people have walked the good Red Road since always. We are connected to the natural rhythms of Father Sky and Mother Earth. We honor the cycles that occur during the day, the year, our life, the lives of all our ancestors. We honor these cycles through ceremony, which we define in your language as 'ritual with heart.' In much of your world, there is no heart in your rituals, just people going through the motions in the hope they will be saved."

She was right! I had stopped going to church when I was twelve, as had my brothers after me. The little child in me knew what most adults have forgotten. There had been no heart; not in the ministers who seemed angry, not in the parishioners who were doing what they thought would insure their spot in heaven. I had felt it years ago.

She saw the recognition in my face and spoke again. "You must renew your spirituality, Charly." I didn't know if I was ready for this. I sat thinking.

Her next words jolted me back. "Change is inevitable. As we grow, we experience change. My people honor those changes, but your people, for the most part, try to insulate themselves from it.

Many fear it. Indigenous people honor life, death and rebirth with the following understanding. We call this tradition the Cycle of Life:

> *Death gives Life*
> *Life gives Rebirth*
> *Rebirth gives Movement*
> *Movement gives Change*
> *Change gives Chaos*
> *Chaos gives Death.*
> *Today is a good day to die.*

I'd heard the saying before, but it hadn't had any meaning. As Spirit Dancer recited it, I began to absorb the truth in it.

My attention returned as she continued. "'Today is a good day to die,' is a warrior's chant before going into battle. Charly, your battle will be with yourself. You are your worst enemy. There are many aspects of who you think you are, that you are not. That which you are not must die for you to become who you are—for you to experience true freedom."

"Spirit Dancer, I'm confused. What do you mean by many aspects I think I am, that I am not?" I asked.

"I will explain this with a story. It is known as the 'Puzzle Theory of Life.' Pay close attention," and she began. "You reside here, on Mother Earth, in the Tonal world we call the Third Dimension. Here there are many limitations to your thinking, to your ability to heal, love, and enjoy life. There is another place where there are no limitations. A place we call the Fifth Dimension. This is where you go in your dream time. In this place we have the ability to know all things, since always and for always. It is what you would call 'infinite intelligence,' something humans reserve only for their God."

I acknowledged and she continued. " In the Fifth Dimension, or Dream State, there are no bodies to limit us, for we reside there as energy. Even your scientists agree that energy just is. It can't be created and it can't be destroyed. To make my point, however, I will separate one piece of this energy, even though in the Fifth Dimension there is no separation. This piece of energy is your 'Life

Force.' It has volunteered to journey to the Third Dimension and enter a physical body. Let's say it is your body before you are born. This infinitely intelligent energy I name Yahoo, to remind you that life is meant to be an adventure."

The name made me smile. "Yahoo, I like that. Go on Spirit Dancer." I said.

"Before leaving the Fifth Dimension, Yahoo creates your "Book of Life". It is like a screenplay in five acts, each act being one of the five aspects of your life; physical, emotional, mental, spiritual and sexual.

"In your Book of Life everything is covered: birth, death, education, relationships, work, money, play, health, adventure, and so on. Before traveling from the Fifth Dimension, to your physical body in the Third Dimension, Yahoo, in effect, has a complete picture of what your life can be. The picture is very large and Yahoo will not be able to carry it through your mother's birth canal, so it is reduced to pieces. Pieces of a puzzle. You arrive in the Third Dimension as a naked, trusting, and innocent baby."

I was mesmerized. As she spoke and gestured, the necklace swayed. If this was a dream, would that be happening? Would I notice all these details? My attention to what she was saying returned.

"Yahoo has your puzzle pieces in a box, but it isn't a normal puzzle box, because it has no picture on the outside. It is blank. Just as you initially forgot my words in your dreams, as an infant you will have no memory of the picture, your Book of Life. There will just be puzzle pieces in the box. In your early years, you are influenced by a combination of everyone surrounding you, including your parents, aunts and uncles, grandparents, school teachers, and civil, social, religious rule makers, and the image makers of radio, television, newspapers, magazines, and movies. They put their collaborative heads together creating the picture that tells you how life really works. This is the information that determines how you will perceive and react to the events in your life, at least early on. This new image is pasted on the outside of your box, and you begin your life according to that picture. Are you with me?" Spirit Dancer asked.

"Sort of," I replied.

"Think of it this way. In your early years you have two pictures telling you how life works: the real one, the one Yahoo created for you in the Fifth Dimension, and the one you believe is real, which was created with the help of your significant influencers. You go along in life living according to the picture on the outside of your box, even though you have disappointments, such as pain, illness, accidents, dashed expectations, and hurtful relationships. You are taught these things are 'normal.' You don't even look at the puzzle pieces on the inside of your box, because the picture on the outside, and your influencers, say you don't know what's best for you. These significant figures repeatedly say, 'Trust us, we are older and wiser.'"

"Well, that sucks!" I blurted out. "How do we get in touch with the real picture if we don't know it's there? If we never look inside the box?" Looking back at my own life I knew she was right, but didn't want to accept it. Suddenly I had a different thought. "Well, what about pleasure? There was some happiness when I was growing up."

"Pleasure, yes. Let me explain," said Spirit Dancer. "Your psychologists say you seek pleasure or you avoid pain. So there are two paths to escape what you call the 'trap.' Remember what's right is what works—at the feeling level. You can learn much by paying more attention to those enjoyable experiences that serve you and others. Unfortunately this is unlikely to happen for most humans, because you have been raised to avoid or discount pleasure. For the most part, your influencers judged pleasure as unproductive, wasteful, or even the 'devil's way.' When you had an enjoyable experience you may have felt guilty, or you dismissed it as an extraordinary event that probably wouldn't happen again, or worse an aberration. You probably discarded it because it didn't fit the picture on the outside of the box. Can you think of an experience in your life that was meaningful and enjoyable whose significance you ignored?"

I thought for a minute, then said, "Sure, when I was in the tenth grade. I went on a weekend canoe trip with my library teacher and some of my classmates. I loved it and after I got back, I started thinking about ways I might be able to make a career out of canoeing. But my father was a lawyer and my mother a teacher, and they both pushed me to go to college and get a "real job". In high school I went to a prep school and there almost all the kids were going to be doctors, lawyers, or businessmen. The kids who didn't want to go into those fields were ostracized."

Spirit Dancer acknowledged with a nod, the opal eye of the eagle twinkled and the copper feathers jingled. "The picture on the outside of the box."

"Yes, what a waste. I know so many people who make big bucks and they're miserable. Didn't you say we had two choices? What's the other one?"

"Pain. Ahh. You will change—or die—when you get to a critical mass of pain. For many it is literally the place where you have to choose between life and death. The alcoholic who gets to the bottom of the barrel, loses everything, and must decide whether to go inside the box and make a significant change, or continue following the picture on the outside of the box and eventually the road to ruin. For many the road to ruin is camouflaged by blocking out, not feeling. Remember what I said before. What's right is what works—at the feeling level.

"In my world, we learn to value our feelings, our intuition. In the human world, you are taught to distrust your feelings and ignore intuition, especially if you are a man. Early in life you begin perfecting the mold that comes from living according to the picture on the outside of the box. You protect or numb your feelings by armoring yourself, putting on a thick outer shell that helps you not feel the pain. When you live according to someone else's truths, you cannot be who you are. Who wants to feel the pain that comes from not being who you are, or the belief you can never be who you are? This is the root of human addictions. Most humans are addicted to something. For some it is a substance like drugs, cigarettes, or sugar. It could be work, thinking too much, television, or romance novels. Whatever the drug of choice, the affect is the same. You anesthetize your feelings, avoiding the pain. Eventually many will come to a crux point for the first, and often most challenging, time. It is then that they must become the warrior, risk the unknown, and explore the inside of the box for a puzzle part, a piece that works."

"How will they know its the right piece? How will I know?" I asked uncertainly.

"You asked about getting in touch with the real picture, the one Yahoo created. You'll know if you have the right piece. It will feel right to you. It will make sense. But first you must learn to trust your instincts. To do that you must wake up. You have always been in touch with your real picture, you just didn't realize it. Don't misunderstand me, there are parts of the picture on the outside of the box that fit the real picture. You'll know what is right for you at the feeling level, and that's part of the challenge.

"This is the Puzzle Theory of Life my friend. It is very important that you grasp this concept. Tell me, what you have heard."

"Well," I began trying to remember, "there are many aspects of who I have become that are in conflict with who I really am. Those aspects I acquired because I was influenced by people and circumstances early in life. I am reaching my own limits of dissatisfaction at not living my life according to what works and feels right for me. To change this, I must face my fear of going against some of the things I was taught by parents and society, and be willing to accept my own truth."

I had been looking down. I raised my eyes and met hers. "Now I know what you mean about dancing on the edge."

I was starting to understand, and I could feel my excitement rise. "For example, all my life I have been a nice guy. No one can be a "nice guy" all the time. It's not real. I've been deceiving myself and others by lying, or withholding the truth, or doing things out of obligation. As a result, I have a diminished sense of myself and a number of shallow relationships.

I was very shy when I was young. I wanted more than anything to be liked. I thought if I was nice enough to people, told them what they wanted to hear, and did things the way they wanted me to, they would like me, or love me, and be my friend. I grew up not knowing what I wanted because my focus was always on what I thought others wanted."

I looked over at Spirit Dancer, who was sitting calmly, smiling slightly, and listening. I paused and thought a moment. "My parents were shy, quiet people. They never imposed themselves on anyone, and wouldn't say no to any request. Whenever they were asked to do something for the church, school, Boy Scouts, or Little League they felt they had to say yes, even if it took away from their own time together. And, they helped draw the picture on my box."

"You have the idea," said Spirit Dancer. "Before I bring this to a close, I want to make two things clear. First, no one has done anything wrong. There is no right or wrong, just consequences. For the most part, your influencers were responsible adults never intending to do you harm. They felt their job was to tell you the way life worked. They had the same responsible adults influencing their lives in their early years. They had their own box with a picture on the outside, as did their parents, and their parents' parents. The only way to break this insane cycle is to take personal responsibility for the choices you make. It all begins with you, and the first step is awareness."

"I understand the first point. What's the second point?" I said.

"This story is meant to describe a life of possibilities. By having the courage to go inside your box and for the first time replace a piece of the picture on the outside, you create a life of adventure. A life that is an exploration during which you get to discover more and more of who you really are. Death gives life . . . Today is a good day to die."

I knew I had more questions, but her image was fading away. I suddenly realized I was exhausted. I took the pad by my bed and made a few notes, and found sleep before my head hit the pillow.

Chapter Two

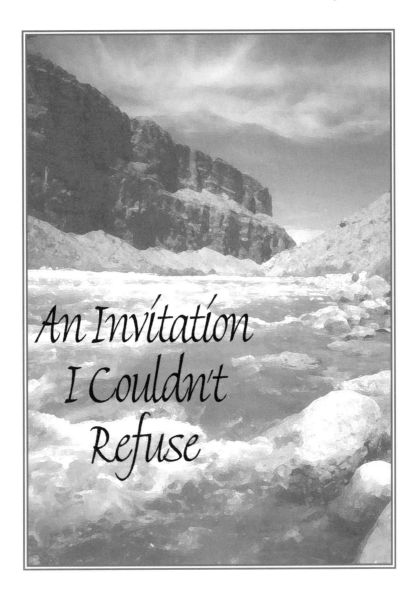

An Invitation I Couldn't Refuse

A couple of days later, I was still amazed by my encounter with Spirit Dancer, not totally trusting that it had been real. While leaving the grocery store, a woman handed me a flyer. The heading jumped out at me. It read, "Life Is An Adventure", describing a free introductory seminar about getting more out of life. I scanned it and thought, "What the heck, I've got nothing but time. I'll go, and maybe I'll get something out of it. Maybe, I'll meet a woman! The price is right, it's free."

The program was held at the local library, and the speaker was less than interesting. I guess you get what you pay for. But as I left, two statements he had made stuck in my mind. "Of myself, I can do no thing (nothing)," and, "I don't know anybody who can handle everything that comes down the road."

"Well, I can," I remember thinking. "I can handle anything that comes down the road." You see, I was blessed with a good mind, was a jack-of-all-trades, and I knew I could do practically anything well if I just put my mind to it.

Nevertheless, something in that statement was disconcerting. So I decided to stop at a local coffee shop, ordered tea and a muffin to go, and pondering the comment, drove to a nearby park. After some thought, I heard a voice in my head say, "If you can handle everything that comes down the road, how come there's a void in your life?" Was the voice really in my head? I looked around and Spirit Dancer began to materialize under a tree. Her white robe seemed almost luminous. I looked around the park to see if anyone else was near. It would have been helpful to know if anyone else could see her. But I was the only one there.

"What do you believe causes your void?" she asked, looking directly into my eyes.

"Well, I've thought about this before." I said, feeling rather proud that I had an answer. "I figure it could only be one of two things. It's either due to the absence of the 'right' woman in my life, or because I have no spiritual connection."

"We both know your happiness must come from within don't we?" She paused to see my reaction.

It wasn't what I wanted to hear. So it wasn't the woman. Damn! I was hoping that would be it. Instead, it was the spiritual thing, something I had been fighting since my teens when I stopped going to church.

I sat there frowning, deep in thought, when she spoke again. "To be able to take the first steps we have discussed, you must find your Power Spot."

"A Power Spot. What's that?" I questioned.

She continued, "It's a physical or imaginary place that speaks to your heart and soul. A place where you feel nurtured and where you can renew and reflect. For some people it is in the mountains, for some the forest, or a cabin at a lake. For others it might be a special space in their home or their community, like a library or a museum. It could even be a backyard, or sitting in a swing in a park. Or a place in your mind: a combination of the best from all the places you've physically been, read about, seen in pictures, or dreamed about. It could be anywhere. You will know when it speaks to you. You will feel alive. It is a place where you can renew. I have said enough. Begin your work. Find your Power Spot. I will return when you really need me. Be well, Charly."

Before I could say anything, she was fading away. My tea was cold, and the muffin no longer looked appealing. I got up to head home. I needed to sleep on this latest revelation.

When I awoke in the morning, I felt better. I seemed to have some sense of purpose. I had to become open to my spirituality. I had no idea what that meant, where or when I would find it, or even how

I would know when I did find it. I just knew it was right. So I made a silent commitment and then immediately felt apprehension. For two-thirds of my life I had closed the door on anything that smacked of religion. What was I getting myself into?

For the next few days I became very cautious. Perhaps I had opened a door to a world I didn't want open. Maybe I had invited something unwanted into my life. I checked and double checked before I crossed the street. I left a light on in the hall outside my bedroom. I took different routes to work. I was nervous, and didn't sleep well, turning small noises in my house into major events. But as time went by, nothing seemed to happen, and the memory of my commitment receded. I fell back into the routine of my mundane and unsatisfying life with little hope of improvement.

Over dinner one night, my roommate and long-time friend Dean made me an offer I couldn't refuse. I had known Dean since I was eight years old. We were inseparable as kids, playing together, publishing a neighborhood newspaper, getting into minor scrapes, like the time we detonated some shotgun shells in his basement with a hammer and nail.

After college, Dean became a sixth grade teacher. For a while he enjoyed it, but soon burned out and headed west for some adventure. He got into mountain climbing, and river rafting. Soon he fell into a job as a commercial raft guide in the Grand Canyon. Silently I was envious of his initiative to change his life. However, I rationalized, he might be having a good time, but he wasn't getting rich. A year before, he had borrowed some money from me to buy a truck. He had paid off most of the principle, but still owed me interest.

On that evening, between bites of pizza he queried me, "How would you like to trade the interest I owe you for a trip in the Grand Canyon next year?"

"Are you serious?" He definitely had my attention.

"Absolutely," he replied.

There was no hesitation on my part. I flashed back to our adolescent years and the great adventures we'd experienced. I was ready for more of that excitement. "Rafting in the Grand Canyon? Hell yes!!! When?"

"May 5th, for twelve days. Plan on being gone for two weeks."

It wouldn't be good timing. I was half owner of a construction company, and May would be the beginning of our peak season. But I heard that voice inside me saying, "Go." The thought struck me, "Who is pushing me to go? Is it me or Spirit Dancer?" It didn't matter. I knew I was going. I spoke to my business partner who wasn't exactly thrilled. But he could see I was determined, and gave a less than enthusiastic, "OK."

Even though it was November and I had six months to wait, my focus turned to the Grand Canyon and this raft adventure. Finally I had something I could really look forward to. Like most Midwesterners, I had only heard of the Grand Canyon. I didn't really know it. I started to read everything I could get my hands on about the Canyon; archaeology, geology, flora and fauna, and human history. The more I read the more excited I became about my trip. It was going to be a wonderful break from the stress of a business that was full of stressful events and stressed-out people.

I had many questions, so Dean began sharing his Grand Canyon experiences and knowledge with me over dinner. A river guide, I soon discovered, has to be a Jack-of-all-trades. He has to know about each aspect of the Canyon so he can interpret it for the passengers. He must be a cook, friend, psychologist, hiker. He needs to learn wilderness first aid, know how to evacuate a passenger in case of injury or other emergency, understand the river and how to navigate it, and do it all with aplomb. With all my reading, I was becoming quite the expert on the Grand Canyon. My anticipation grew and I began feeling strange expectations, but I didn't allow myself such a luxury and pushed those feelings down.

I came home from work one day to find huge maps of the Grand Canyon taped all over the dining room walls. One was an aerial view of the Canyon, and the others were multicolored and, except for their artistic flair, didn't make any sense to me. I looked at Dean quizzically.

"This is an aerial view of the Canyon, and these," pointing to the brightly colored ones, "are geological maps showing all the fault zones. The colors represent the different rock formations. If you'll make the spaghetti, I'll give you a Grand Canyon geology lesson."

"Cool. Let me get the water going."

I filled our eight quart pot with water, added a touch of salt and olive oil, set it on the stove and put the flame on high. "I'm all ears, Dean. Take me to geology heaven."

"This will just be an overview. But, when you get to the Canyon and see the real thing, it'll make a lot more sense having this background." I grabbed a chair and settled in. He began the lecture.

"There are three types of rock in the Canyon: sedimentary, igneous and metamorphic. Sedimentary rock includes sandstone, limestone and shale. Sandstone is formed in either a desert or ocean environment. Limestone forms in a shallow ocean, around five to six hundred feet in depth, and shales are made up of very small granules of silt and mud deposited just off shore. Igneous rock is either lava or granite. Both are molten rock. Lava is extruded or ejected from within the earth and granite is intruded or injected into cracks in underlying rock structures. Metamorphic rock can be any of the ones I just described, but has been metamorphosed, meaning the crystalline structure of the rock has been altered due to extreme heat and pressure.

"These rocks form three distinct structures. The harder rock, like some sandstones, limestone, granite, and metamorphic rock, form into cliffs which can rise right out of the river. Some of the softer sandstones will form ledges. The softest rocks will form slopes because they are easily eroded."

"OK." I said hesitantly. My brain was frantically trying to file this information into the right folder, and having some trouble.

"All rock is made up of material that was other rock at an earlier time. It was eroded, predominantly by wind and rain. and carried primarily by rivers from the mountains to the ocean. The faster the water the bigger the debris it can carry. As the water slows down, the larger sediment drops out first, and then the next smaller and so on until there is no more sediment. That's why you will see sand dunes along the ocean margins, either on shore or just off shore. The granules that make up sandstone are larger than the silt and mud granules, and being heavier, drop out of the current near the shore. A little farther off shore the silt and mud begins dropping out. This will eventually form into shale. Finally, in the quiet ocean away from shore, untold numbers of sea creatures known as phytoplankton die off and their shells, composed of calcium carbonate, fall to the ocean bottom. Over eons these become a kind of primordial ooze that eventually hardens due to the pressure of the water above, forming limestone. So wherever you find limestone quarries, you know that place was once covered by an ocean."

"All right. That makes sense." I tried to organize my thinking so I would remember this lesson when I finally saw the real thing.

"When we get to the Canyon you will find nine sedimentary rock layers, with the youngest on top of the oldest. Below that will be other sedimentary rock layers plus igneous and metamorphic rock. The youngest rock in the Canyon is around 240 million years old, about the time the dinosaurs began. The oldest rock, called schist, is around 1.7 billion years old."

"Really? 1.7 billion? That's mind boggling," I said with amazement.

"That's enough for now. There's a lot more information in the river guide book I gave you. Study hard. There will be a test tomorrow evening." He pretended to dismiss me like one of his sixth-grade students when he was teaching. For a moment there, I actually thought he was serious. Then he cracked a big smile and headed into the kitchen.

After grabbing a beer out of the refrigerator he poked at the spaghetti, got a strand and flung it against the kitchen cabinet.

"Not quite done yet. Are we putting something on this?" Now he was looking at me.

Absent-mindedly, I found the pesto sauce, and waving it in the air I said "This is great, I'll study those books later. What I want to know now is what will a typical day be like on our trip?"

Guzzling his beer, he settled in a kitchen chair and looked contentedly off in the distance for a few moments, visualizing the river. "We start getting everybody up as soon as the coffee is ready, have breakfast about twenty minutes later, clean up and load the boats. Since you'll be going as part of the crew, you'll actually be helping with all this." I nodded. "Then, depending on our location, the weather, the kind of group we have, you know, whether they're into hiking for instance, we'll either take a hike, give a talk, or head on downstream. If we talk, it could be about what to expect that day on the river, something about the geology, something historical about the native peoples, stuff like that. We hike almost every day. Some hikes are as much as 14-16 miles, some as short as a quarter mile. And we never force a passenger to go on the hike. They can stay back at the boats and read if they want."

"I remember you saying that one of the crew always leads the hike and one brings up the rear, right?" I chimed in.

"Right, and if the water is low, we'll do a hike waiting for it to come up. The water fluctuates because of Glen Canyon Dam. You know that Glen Canyon Dam creates Lake Powell upstream in Utah?" I nodded and began straining the spaghetti.

He continued, "Overnight the water flow is decreased because there is less energy demand. At the end of the work day, about four or five o'clock, people head home. The plants and office buildings need less energy, so they cut the electrical output back by letting less water through the turbines. This causes the river level to go down. About six or seven in the morning, the gates are opened and the turbines start cranking. If we're downstream, say at mile 48, we're actually about 63 miles away from the dam. That's about sixteen hours as the river flows. So water that is released at six in the morning won't arrive where we are until ten at night. If we're camped at mile 48 like I said, we have to be prepared for the water to come up during the night. This means anticipating the rise and adjusting the boats before we go to bed. About the time we're getting on the river the next morning, the water will start going down again. Depending on when we leave, if we're not prepared for this, we might come back from a hike and find our boats high and dry."

"Wow, that's a lot to remember." I said stuffing my mouth full of spaghetti.

Dean took a bite and chewed. "After a while, it comes naturally. We'll stop for lunch at a place that provides shade and maybe some diversion."

"Like what?".

"Like a swimming hole fed by a waterfall, or a cave carved by Spring floods. After lunch we'll head downstream, maybe take another hike, or stop at some historic spot like an ancient habitation site, or granaries where the ancient peoples used to store food. We need to plan ahead, though, because we like to reach camp in time for people to relax while we prepare dinner. It's nice to eat while it's still light. The crew cleans up, and by then it's dark. We've had a long, active day, and everybody's ready to get horizontal."

"Does everyone camp together?" I wanted to know.

"We basically have one camp, but everyone takes off and lays claim to their own little sleeping area for privacy. Well, that's a typical day. Some days will have big rapids, other days the river will be fairly mellow. But, there will be rapids every day, and there will be two days in particular when we'll run through one big rapid after another for thirty-one miles."

The phone rang and interrupted Dean, but our conversation was really over. He answered it, and as I cleaned up the kitchen, I was in my own little world trying to imagine what it would be like sleeping under the Milky Way hundreds of miles away from city lights.

Chapter Three

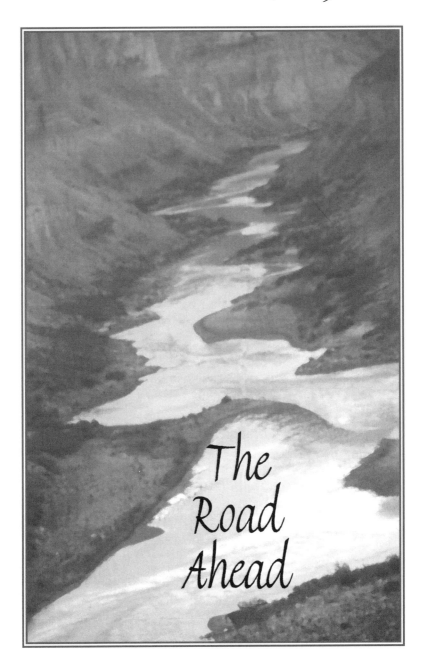

The
Road
Ahead

The closer I got to the trip the more excited I became. With a couple of weeks to go, I was so focused on the Grand Canyon I couldn't concentrate at work. At night, I made lists of what I needed to take. During the day I was on the phone trying to scrounge needed items from friends and family. It seemed like a lot. Good rain suit, long underwear, shorts, bathing suits, shoes that could get wet, a hat, sweater, light jacket, lightweight long sleeve shirt and pants (for sun protection), personal hygiene items, camera and film, cup, plate and utensils, some dress up clothes for party night (the last night of the trip), whatever drinks I wanted. It seemed endless, and that didn't include the tent, sleeping bag, ground cloth, and sleeping pad.

Finally, it was the night before departure and I was ready. The river trip was to start on May 18, and I decided to drive because I had never driven to the Southwest. I was curious about the country between Michigan and Flagstaff, Arizona. My route would be Interstate 80 to Denver, I-70 to Moab, Utah, then south through Utah and the Navajo Reservation in Northwest Arizona, across the Painted Desert, and on to Flagstaff. According to my calculations, it was about 2,400 miles. I figured that would take me three long days or four reasonable ones. I opted for the reasonable approach.

Dean was already in Arizona, having left in late March for the river season. He was on the River and would be off a couple of days before our trip began. I was excited and nervous. There would be several firsts for me on this trip. First solo road trip, first time driving through the Rocky Mountains, first time in the Arizona, first time in the Grand Canyon.

On April 30, at 6:30 in the morning I closed my front door and stepped into my Opel GT. I had a small cooler with fruit, sandwiches and juice, enough for a couple of days. I wanted to avoid fast food because it was generally laden with fat and sugar, and would only make me tired. I headed south on the Southfield freeway, into Detroit, turned west on I-94, and settled back. The radio was playing a medley of Bob Seger hits and I was cruising. My plan was to hit Omaha, Nebraska before finding a motel. Omaha was almost 800 miles, and I figured if I made it that far on the first day, I could take it easy the rest of the way.

I was finally on my way. This was such an adventure. Spring was showing up everywhere. The trees were sprouting, and there were so many shades of green. It was all so fresh, as if I had been in a coma for years and this was my first day out. I had just turned 36 and felt like a kid in a candy shop. I couldn't ever remember feeling this free, or this lighthearted. As I drove along Lake Michigan towards the Indiana border, I looked out at the clear blue sky above and the whitecaps on the windy lake, and let out a long, loud "Yahoo!!!"

I flew past Chicago and then Joliet. This was my first taste of the real Midwest. The grass was lush, farmers were out working their fields, the sun was shining, and I was energized. When I crossed the Mississippi River at Davenport, Iowa, I thought about one of my high school heroes, Mark Twain. I looked out at that huge, wide muddy river and tried to put myself in Huck Finn's shoes. I imagined the excitement he must have felt on that rickety old raft adventure.

Iowa was even greener than Illinois and I flew across into Nebraska and the outskirts of Omaha by around 7:30 p.m. Good timing. The next morning I was on the road by 6 a.m. and discovered that Nebraska is . . . well there's no other way to say it . . . a very long state without much variety. Today I wanted to cover the 600 miles to Denver, and I hoped to make it there in time to have dinner with Jim, an old friend from high school who was struggling as an architect. He had invited me to spend the night.

The miles barely crept by and I couldn't find anything but country music on the radio. A lot of songs about heartache and faithless men. Before I got to Lincoln, I turned it off. With no musical or scenic distractions, I began to think about my life back in Michigan. I decided when I returned, I would start looking for another job. Even though it was my own construction business, there was little pleasure in going to work. I wanted a job that didn't feel like "work".

I started to focus on my personal life when I noticed an older man walking along the shoulder. He was obviously getting up there in age, but walked with a confidence and briskness that was ageless. I had received warnings from family and friends about picking up hitchhikers, but having done plenty of hitchhiking myself, I felt I kind of knew the ropes. The Opel seemed to swerve to the shoulder on its own and I found myself waving to the man. He got into the small car with ease, and we found a spot for his one suitcase. We introduced ourselves. His name was George and he had also left Omaha that morning, on a whim, to visit his daughter. He was bound for Ogallala, still in Nebraska but almost to the Wyoming border. He revealed that he had just celebrated his 91st birthday. He hadn't driven for several years, but that certainly wasn't slowing him down any. He told me he hiked in the hills around Omaha every day.

The conversation turned to my destination and I asked him if he'd ever seen the Grand Canyon.

He looked pensively out the side window and then began to reminisce. "I think it was 1938 that I first hiked the Bright Angel Trail. There wasn't much going on in the Canyon in those days. I think they had a few mule trips every year. I ran into one of those mules when I was hiking. We were both trying to cross a suspension bridge over the Colorado River, down by that Phantom Ranch. I wasn't about to let that critter get the best of me, and I finally backed him off the bridge." He looked at me and winked and I wondered if that part of the story was true.

I told him my plans were to join my roommate's rafting company and partake in a 12-day float trip. He thought for a minute and then launched into the story of John Wesley Powell's 1869 exploratory expedition into the Great Unknown. He was a good storyteller and I had goose bumps and felt the hair raise on the back of my neck as he described the one-armed man's adventure through the Canyon.

I was fascinated by his experiences and wisdom, and we talked for a couple of hours. I finally asked him if he'd like to go back someday. He thought about it for a good minute, then said, "I think so, but your trip sounds better than mine. I bet it's easier to raft the Colorado River than to hike the Canyon."

After that he dozed for a while, and I thought about what a gift it was to meet this unique man. I knew I would always remember this encounter. I pulled off the Interstate in Ogallala and dropped him at his daughter's place. She had no idea that he was coming, but welcomed him with open arms. I left them sitting on her front porch.

Returning to I-80, a sign announced the Colorado border 28 miles away. I became very excited. Colorado and the Rocky Mountains. I think I imagined the mountains appearing magically as soon as I crossed over the state line. That didn't happen. Not at Julesburg just inside Colorado, not at Sterling about 60 miles into the state.

I found myself talking out loud, "It's the Rocky Mountains for God's sake. They're huge. Where are they?" I drove another fifty miles to Ft. Morgan, and still didn't see the mountains. I was perplexed and impatient. The mountains had become a symbol of progress to me. I knew when I saw them, that I'd really be on my way. Then I saw them, at first hidden by haze, but finally standing out far in the distance. The Front Range of the Rocky Mountains. I pulled over and popped in a John Denver tape. Turning it up full blast, I sang "Rocky Mountain High" as loudly as I could. It was corny, but exhilarating. No doubt I wasn't the first to do that, nor would I be the last. Denver was now less than an hour away. I called my friend Jim to get directions and continued on singing with John, "Sunshine on my shoulder makes me happy . . ."

Over dinner I heard all about Jim's adventures in Colorado; hiking, biking, climbing, and kayaking. He'd been to Rocky Mountain National Park several times and told me about hiking around the headwaters of the Colorado. He said that near Grandby the River is just a trickle. He had a number of stories to tell and we talked way too long, considering I wanted to be on my way early. He was living a good life even though he was still struggling to build his architectural business. I was very attracted to the active lifestyle he described and very drawn to the mountains. Instead of going due west across Colorado to Moab, Jim suggested I head southwest out of Denver towards the San Luis Valley, Durango, and the Four Corners area where Colorado, New Mexico, Arizona and Utah all connect. Why not, I was flexible.

Morning rose way too soon, and after a hearty breakfast, we said our good-byes and I headed toward the mountains.

As I drove into the Rockies I was overcome with emotion. To drive along a two lane highway with snowcapped mountains on both sides was so dramatic for this Midwestern boy. Until now I had only dreamed of being in the mountains, usually after watching a movie or reading *National Geographic Magazine*. There is an ever-present air of freedom in those mountain peaks and valleys. The air was fresh, the colors deep, and at that moment the possibilities seemed endless. For the first time in my life I knew how I wanted to feel, every day. Just like this. Briefly I flirted with the idea of moving to Colorado. My thoughts were interrupted by a bald eagle soaring overhead. Another first.

Passing through Fairplay wondering about the derivation of the name, I looked off to the west and realized I must be seeing Mt. Elbert glistening with pure white snow, just like the Colorado license plates on the car in front of me. As described in the road map, the 14,433 foot peak is the highest Fourteener, as the fifty-two 14,000+ foot peaks in Colorado are nicknamed. I then headed west on Route 50, over Monarch Pass and the Continental Divide at 11,312 feet. All water from here on would be drawn west and south, to the Pacific or the Gulf of California, while water falling on the eastern slope ran to the Mississippi River or the Gulf of Mexico.

I stopped in Gunnison and called Louise, a friend of Jim's who lives in Durango. She was very nice and invited me to spend the night on her couch. Durango was a small town at an elevation of 6,500 feet. It felt as if I'd entered onto the set of an old western movie. Men walked around in cowboy boots and hats, and women wore western skirts and blouses. Louise welcomed me with a wonderful dinner, breakfast, and sandwiches for the road. This must be western hospitality! We talked about what I could expect crossing Arizona and she showed me on the map how to get to Flagstaff through the Navajo Reservation.

Turns out Louise is a river guide in the Grand Canyon and she knows the route well. Before I left she shared a few stories about her trips. On one trip, she awoke in the middle of the night to find her boat floating. Somehow it had slipped its earthly bond. Not far downstream lay Lava Falls, the grandmother of big rapids in the Grand Canyon. To make matters worse, she only had one oar. I could feel my stomach knot up as she described how she was finally able to get the boat to shore just upstream of the roaring rapid. Her enthusiasm for being in the Canyon added to my own excitement and curiosity.

I drove west out of Durango, climbed to about 10,000 feet, and then began my descent towards Cortez and the Four Corners area. Just east of Cortez, as I passed the sign for Mesa Verde National Park, my thoughts returned to last night's conversation. Louise had told me about the magnificent cliff dwellings built by the Anasazi Indians preserved in the Park. I was intent on arriving in Flagstaff before dinner, and knew I would see Anasazi ruins in the Canyon, so I made a mental note to schedule a day or two on my return trip for exploration in and around Mesa Verde.

I did succumb to one tourist trap at the Four Corners area, the only place in the United States where four states meet. Tourists from all over the world get down on all fours and place one foot in Colorado, one in New Mexico, one hand in Utah and one in Arizona. Pretty neat, but time to move on.

If I thought Nebraska represented wide open spaces, the Navajo Reservation shattered that belief. These were really wide open spaces, a huge desert plateau at around 6,000 feet. There were few trees, just rolling hills and sandstone formations. At a non-town-town called Tonolea, I touched the northwest edge of the Hopi Reservation. I remembered in my reading how the Hopi and Navajo have long been adversaries. When the US Government intervened in the disagreements over the boundaries of their reservation land, the solution made no one happy. The result was placing the Hopi Reservation right in the southwest section of the Navajo Reservation. So the Hopi had to learn to live surrounded by a people who called their ancestors, "ancient enemy," one translation of Anasazi. Driving through this land made me want to know more about the history of the Native Americans in the southwest. Having been a student of American History in college provided almost no information about the people and their culture. I knew I couldn't rely on my history books to know the truth about these people. Perhaps I could learn from the source.

I continued through Tuba City where a left turn would have taken me into the Hopi reservation and towns with names like Hotevilla, Kykotsinaovi, Second Mesa and Keams Canyon. A few miles west of Tuba City, Route 160 ended at Highway 89. If I traveled fifty miles to the right and north, I would have crossed over the Navajo Bridge spanning the Colorado River. Sixty-nine miles to my left and to the south, and 3500 feet higher in elevation, was Flagstaff. I was tempted to head north, my curiosity for the Grand Canyon heightened by its proximity. But knowing I would pass this way again tomorrow, I headed for Flagstaff and the last leg of my road journey.

I drove by Cameron and stopped at the trading post there. It had been established in the nineteenth century as a true trading post, and I marveled at the foresight of one person who could have foreseen this isolated spot as a place that would grow in influence and importance into the next century. I'm certain there was some luck, but its physical presence more than a hundred years later, bears dramatic testament to the power of a vision.

Just south of Cameron, Highway 64 offers a road to the Eastern entrance to the Grand Canyon, 56 miles away. Again I was tempted, but as with Mesa Verde, I didn't want my first experience to be a quick snapshot. Another place on my to do list for a future time.

The San Francisco peaks, the highest land mass in Arizona , came into view. It was mid-afternoon, the sky was blue, and I could feel the dry desert air sucking moisture from my skin. I was on a long climb to 7,000 feet, and my destination of Flagstaff, Arizona. I enjoyed the uniqueness of the mural before me. The Painted Desert and sprawling Navajo Reservation were behind me. At this elevation, magnificent Ponderosa Pines stood on both sides of the highway, and beautiful spring clouds floated peacefully above the mountains.

What an amazing country! I'd been driving four days and experienced such diversity, from urban Midwest to farmland both east and west of the Mississippi, huge rivers bordering vast tracts of open plains, mountains rising straight up dividing the country into eastern and western watersheds, high desert, low desert, and now a mountain born from volcanic activity rising out of a high plateau that itself had been formed by unseen and unimaginably powerful and dynamic geological forces. I had already experienced so much. I suddenly felt like Powell on his first exploration of this area. What could possibly lay ahead?

Chapter Four

Meeting the Crew

Before he took off for Arizona, Dean instructed me to go to Macy's, a coffee shop on South Beaver Street, when I arrived in Flagstaff. I called him at the number he had given me, and he came over. We split a pastry that was big enough for three. Since I hadn't showered for a couple of days, his comments about me already looking like a River Rat were appropriate. Dean never was very subtle. We headed over to the raft company's warehouse north of town. The view of the San Francisco Peaks looming out the front window was awesome. The warehouse was sitting in an open flood plain and was actually just an old house with a large, open garage. For dinner Dean fixed the "River Rat Special", a supper of beans, rice and tortillas. He informed me this was his staple, since guides only made about $50 a day, and after all it was the Southwest.

We talked awhile about my drive out and then the conversation turned to what would be happening in the morning. The rest of the crew would show up around 8:00 a.m., we'd pack the food in coolers with blocks of ice on the bottom, load all the gear on a big two and a half ton stake truck called "Blue", named for it's sky-blue paint job, and take a couple of hours for last minute shopping for stuff like sunscreen, film, beer, or soda for the trip, and lunch. Then we would head north on Route 89A, back in the direction I had just been, about 140 miles out of the mountains and into the desert to Lees Ferry in northern Arizona. I learned that all raft trips take off from Lees Ferry. There we would inflate the rafts, put all the gear on, and spend the night. The passengers would be bussed up from Flagstaff the next morning.

Weary from four days of driving, I threw my bag on the floor, and bid Dean good night. I must have fallen asleep immediately, because the next thing I remember was the smell of bacon cooking. It was morning and Dean already had the coffee going and was scrambling eggs. My head buzzed with excitement and questions, but I sensed Dean's mind was on the events of the day, so we ate in relative silence. I packed my personal gear in two waterproof black bags given to me for the trip, and one by one the crew arrived.

The first was a surprise. Dean introduced me to Marian. I hadn't expected any women on this trip and never imagined one of the guides would be female. Marian was a tall, slim woman with a very pleasant smile, a warm voice, and a lot of energy. She was from a well-to-do family back East, and I learned she had been to a prestigious women's college and was working as an executive secretary in Los Angeles in the early 70's when a friend convinced her to go on a Grand Canyon raft trip. The rest as they say, was history. Within a year she had left her job, enrolled in a California whitewater school to learn about reading the river and rowing a raft, had run rivers in California and Idaho for a couple years, and ended up becoming one of the first women oar guides in the Canyon. I remember wondering how well she would handle the big rafts and all the heavy lifting Dean had described to me.

Next to arrive was James Lord, a "trainee" who would be rowing the baggage boat. He lived in Southern California and was a financial consultant. He was about 5'10" and seemed rather quiet. James would be by himself most of the time, because the rafting company's liability insurance didn't cover paying passengers riding with trainees. Since I wasn't a paying passenger, it would be all right for me to ride with him if I wanted to. I was struck by his last name and thought to myself, "Hmmm, Lord and Heavenrich, now that would be an interesting partnership." If I had remembered my spiritual quest, I might have taken those words more to heart. Truth is, I was thinking more about a business relationship since we both had business backgrounds. We joked about business cards with the name, "Lord and Heavenrich, Financial Consultants."

The last to arrive, just before eight, were Wally and Greg. Wally was tall lanky and handsome with an easy smile, a friendly hello, and a very quick wit. He was going to college at Northern Arizona in Flagstaff, studying biology. By far the most energetic of the group, I took an immediate liking to him. Greg was the trip leader. He was in his early thirties and very quiet. Dean told me he was from Utah and worked the oil fields as a rigger during the off season. He was married to a beautiful woman and had no children. He looked very much like a lean cowboy with his boots and ten gallon hat. He seemed to have a good relationship with everybody. In fact, this was obviously a very close group. I guess after putting their lives on the line for ten or twelve trips each summer, you'd either be close or you wouldn't be there at all. Without any prompting everybody set to work. Marian sorted out and tied up the life jackets, one for each passenger and a spare for each boat.

Wally called over to me, "Hey Charly, come on, I'm gonna put you to work." We packed the coolers with produce, dairy, meat and eggs, each separately. The canned goods went in W.W.II surplus 20 cal. ammo cans. It seemed like enough for an army. Dean and Greg loaded the gray boats, frames and eleven-foot sky-blue oars, four for each of the five boats. Two were spares in case one or both broke, or floated away. I thought that was a very good idea. When Wally and I were done with the coolers, I asked Marian what she was doing.

"Packing the shitters," she replied with a grin. The "shitters" were more 20 cal. ammo cans that would carry out the human waste. A small detail that Dean hadn't mentioned during our dinner conversations. We packed enough toilet paper for what seemed like a month and included powdered Clorox to "prevent the buildup of methane gas in the filling and full cans." Sounded like a good idea to me. I couldn't imagine one of those things blowing up.

As if hearing my thoughts, Dean told me a story.

"Last year," he began, a remembering smile spreading across his face, "VK, the owner of the company, rowed our final trip of the river season. Instead of going back to the warehouse in Flag, he decided to drive it back to his home in Pacific Grove, California. He also chose to put off unloading the truck til later. Later turned out to be early spring. He removed one of the shitter cans, and without thinking, unsealed the lid. Because of methane buildup, it blew up all over the warehouse." Everybody knew the story except me, but they had all stopped working to listen, and enjoyed a good laugh.

I cringed at the thought of what had happened to VK as we all went back to our work.

We added a four burner stove, four bulbous propane tanks, and assorted other essentials, like a volleyball and net and horseshoes. Finally, the crew loaded their personal gear and we closed the gates on Blue.

We drove south towards Flagstaff, turned East on old Route 66, and stopped at a supermarket in East Flag for soda, beer, lunch, and last minute personal items. We then headed out of town on 89A. Dean, Wally , James and I were in the back on top of the gear.

Just out of town we passed the summit, slightly over 7000 feet in elevation. Laid out before me down the mountain road was the desert and the Navajo Reservation I had crossed yesterday.

The anticipation was almost too much as we began our 140 mile journey to Lees Ferry. I couldn't take my eyes off the stark beauty of the landscape. Hot desert winds hit me in the face, but I paid it no mind, and kept pushing away the feeling that something very unexpected was about to happen. After all, this was just another vacation. I'd already been rafting on the Colorado River in Utah. Twice, in fact. How different could this be? I figured I'd have the same result: a nice getaway with a few adventures and some good memories pasted in a scrapbook.

About three hours later we slowed as the truck traveled down a winding curve through a depression cut out of the desert. Coming out into the open again, I saw a bridge and had my first glimpse of the Colorado River 425 feet below. It was beautiful. My heart sped up as I looked down at the iridescent green water I had been anticipating for so many months.

The truck turned right, and we headed down a paved road with eroded sandstone cliffs to our left. Ten minutes later we were crossing over a bridge spanning the Paria, a small creek that was just barely flowing. The liquid was gray-brown and seemed thicker than water.

In a few minutes we arrived at Lees Ferry. It was not what I expected. Instead of wilderness, what I saw was a floating parking lot with a half dozen boats of varying shapes and sizes from other companies. The beach was a sloping gravel-filled area strewn with river gear.

Our driver backed Blue to within twenty feet of the green Colorado River, and Greg placed a large rock behind one of the wheels to prevent any unwanted movement. Immediately the easygoing, relaxed pace and conversation ended, and shifted to an efficient business-like operation as everyone went into action. I was amazed at the cooperation and team work, usually without any verbal cues.

The boats were dumped off the truck and Marian and Wally began unrolling and lining them up on the beach. An electrical outlet was located just off the boat ramp and Dean plugged in the blower and began inflating the boats. As they swelled, it was like they too were coming alive and becoming excited about this adventure. Someone yelled for me to grab the frames, and as each eighteen foot boat was filled, I placed a frame in the center.

I watched Wally select a boat and begin securing the frame with straps and loading it with gear. Each guide had his or her own equipment and methods of preparation. A cooler was loaded into each boat, 20 cal. cans, oar locks, oars and spares were tied hanging off the sides, five gallon water jugs, a throw line, floatation pillow, and something called a gay bag were added. I learned the gay bag was vinyl and would be used for storing the passenger's waterproof black bags containing their personal gear and sleeping bags.

Time flew and in three hours most of the work was done. Everyone breathed a sigh of relief, and there was an automatic shift back into a more relaxed pace, as business was forgotten. We piled back into Blue for a five mile ride to Marble Canyon Lodge. The day had been long and we knew we had twelve more days ahead of us. Dinner was eaten relatively fast with simple catch-up conversation. The drive back to Lees Ferry was quiet and we all looked forward to a good night's sleep.

Chapter Five

Welcome Home, Brother

The night was spent sleeping on the boats or on shore. It was amazing lying there looking up into a velvet black sky. The stars were so close, I was sure I could touch them with an outstretched hand. The Milky Way, a minor galaxy among ten billion galaxies, appeared cloud-like in the clear Arizona night sky. The sound of a small rapid downstream played softly in my ears, lulling me to sleep; but there was so much sensory stimulation that I woke several times during the night. These were sounds I wasn't used to hearing in Michigan. Each time I opened my eyes I was treated to a most impressive celestial display. I knew I needed to sleep, but I was tempted to lay awake and watch the stars' movement. I could see constellations I had only read about in my college astronomy books.

In the morning we shared a breakfast of river coffee (made by pouring coffee grounds into boiling water), melons, bananas, and pastries. Each guide then made the final adjustments on their boats and relaxed until the passengers arrived. At about 10:00 a.m. a big bus appeared and sixteen people spilled out for their first look at the Grand Canyon. Actually, the Canyon didn't officially start until 0.4 mile downstream, but no one cared about technicalities. They were jet-lagged and weary from their long plane rides from the East, Southeast, Northwest, and West. Many had been too wired to sleep the night before, and had just spent over three hours riding in a bus, wondering as I had, when they would get their first glimpse of the Grand Canyon.

They came in all shapes and sizes. There was Jane, a gentle woman appearing to be in her late forties who seemed out of place. Richard, also forty-something, was definitely muscle tone challenged, but he had a friendly smile and a warm handshake as I introduced myself. He told me this was his first camping trip and he was both excited and nervous. Frank was a corpulent thirty-something who seemed to be in his own world. As soon as he got off the bus he removed his shirt revealing an ample belly and hair covering his chest and shoulders. He went down and announced his presence to the river and to anyone else who was interested. His voice echoed off the cliffs upstream. So much for tranquillity in the Canyon. The rest of the lineup included three couples who had known each other for years, three men in their fifties or sixties, and two forty-something women with their twenty-three year old daughters.

Once again the crew shifted into high gear. Introductions were made and people were fitted with life jackets. Their individual black bags and other gear were loaded on the boats and stored in the gay bags. Most careful attention was paid to the burlap sacks which contained beer and soft drinks. I learned river guides are ever careful about insuring the safety of beer.

While the crew worked, Greg took the rest of us over to a shady grove of tamarisk trees for a lesson on safety. He began by having each passenger say where they were from. I learned that Jane was from San Francisco, Frank had come all the way from Boston, and Richard was from Southfield, Michigan. I had grown up in Birmingham, next door to Southfield. I commented on the irony of traveling 2,400 miles to meet one of my neighbors. The three couples were from Kansas City, the four older men had been to college together years before in Texas, and the women were from Florida.

Next, Greg launched into the safety talk. "Each of your guides will add more to what I have to say, and I won't take a lot of your time here because it's hot and we want to get on the water. But there are a few things you need to know to make sure this is a safe trip for all of us. Charly, put on this jacket and I'll use you to demonstrate."

I put on the life jacket as he continued. It was starting to get warm even in the shade.

"While it is unusual for a boat to flip, it does happen. Also on rare occasions, a passenger will find himself or herself in the river, involuntarily. If this should happen and there is a boat nearby, the guide will throw you a line, like this one." He picked up a canvas bag he'd brought over with him. It had a loop of rope hanging out one end.

"We will throw this a little downstream of you, grab it, and turn over on your back facing away from the boat." He turned around with the rope over his shoulder to demonstrate, then looked back around to make sure everyone understood.

"Hold on to the line with both hands tight against your chest, and let us pull you to the boat." He stressed the "us" part of the sentence. "When we get you to the boat, face it, and grab onto the boat safety line with both hands." He turned and indicated the rafts where the others were still busy. "You'll see the safety lines around the top of each raft when we go back. On the count of three, either a guide or one of the passengers will pull you up and in. You can help by kicking your feet as you are being pulled. Charly, come here and let me demonstrate."

I squatted in front of him and he took hold of my shoulders, counted to three and stood me up. Then he said, "If it's done right, Charly would end up on top of me in the boat."

Frank commented in his loud voice, "Looks easy enough, but I don't plan to be going in the water."

Greg ignored the comment and went on. "Thanks Charly. Now, if a boat flips, you will usually be thrown clear. If you should find yourself under the boat, find the frame overhead, walk your hands upstream, against the flow of the current, to the edge of the raft and pop up." He demonstrated by grabbing the air in a walking motion over his head.

"Then swim to the upstream end of the boat, against the current, and either pull yourself up on top of the overturned raft, or just hang on until someone helps you out of the water. We will be running close together in the big rapids, so there will likely be another boat nearby."

"What if there isn't another boat?" came a panicked voice. I looked around at the other passengers. They were all listening intently and several looked very anxious, especially Jane, who had posed the question. I smiled, and remembered that Jane had looked a little out of place when I had first seen her getting out of the bus.

It was evident that Greg had given this talk many times. "Sometimes you will get separated from your raft when it flips. Look for another boat, and immediately do what the guide tells you. If there is no other boat nearby, swim across the current and get to shore as soon as you can. The most significant danger down here is hypothermia from the cold water. You don't want to be in it any longer than necessary."

As warm as it was getting, it was hard to imagine being cold enough to experience hypothermia.

Greg continued, "I apologize for laying this on you right away, but it is important that you understand the safety procedures before we get on the river. There are no rapids for the first eight miles, so you can relax and enjoy. Like I said earlier, boats do flip down here, but this is a very experienced crew, and our safety record is excellent. We only lose one or two passengers per trip."

A couple of heads jerked up and Greg smiled, "Just kidding. Some of these guides have never flipped, the rest only once or twice in over fifty trips. We'll be talking about a lot of things today, including more safety information on the boats, proper hygiene, logistics when we stop for lunch, and then more stuff when we get to camp. You'll be overloaded with information, but after today it will be all about the Canyon. You can choose the boat you want to ride on each day. The only exception is James's boat. It's got all the kitchen gear and will be carrying out the garbage, stuff to recycle, and human waste."

"Sounds like a good boat to avoid then," Frank piped up again with a smirk on his face. I didn't think I was going to like this guy.

Finally, we were ready to begin our journey. Passengers selected their raft for the day and we shoved off. It was finally happening. The Grand Canyon awaited us less than a half mile downstream. Not knowing any of the others well, except for Dean, I decided to ride with James. I wanted to hear more about his training as a river guide, and I thought we might compare notes about his financial consulting and my master's degree in business. I was still thinking about that unique partnership, Lord and Heavenrich. I untied James's boat, pushed off from the shore and hopped on, eager to be away from cars, phones and the mad dash of making a living.

The Colorado is fairly wide at Lees Ferry, and glassy smooth. Remembering that the first rapid isn't until mile 8, I found a spot at the front of the raft and settled back to enjoy the ride.

As we entered the current that would carry us downstream for the next 226 miles, a rush of unexpected feelings interrupted my reverie. Instantaneously tears welled up in my eyes, a shiver raced down my spine, and goose bumps sprouted on my skin. There's no other way to say this. I had the clear sensation of nonphysical arms wrapping around me and a voice from nowhere saying "welcome home, brother, welcome home." Suddenly thoughts of Spirit Dancer entered my mind. I looked around to see if her holographic image was with me in the raft, but I only saw James rhythmically rowing the boat. With the excitement of planning the trip, I had practically forgotten my strange encounters with the medicine woman, my assignment to find a power spot, and my commitment to renew my spirituality.

Did this have something to do with that? These feelings were so strong and unexpected. I had no idea how to respond, so I just sat there overwhelmed and wondered what I had gotten myself into.

The Canyon walls were rising above me as we gently floated downstream, but I barely noticed. I was in some other dimension. James's voice was barely audible in the background describing the Kaibab Limestone as it appeared on the left side of the river. I was to learn that this formation was the capstone rock in the Grand Canyon because it was the top layer of rock. At the deepest point in the Canyon it would hover 4,600 vertical feet above us .

We passed under the Navajo Bridge some 4 miles downstream. It would be the last man-made structure and crossing point for 84 miles. As we entered the shadow of the bridge, I felt my body shudder. I was coming back to my senses, or perhaps leaving them, I wasn't certain. In any event, I suddenly remembered Spirit Dancer's words about finding my Power Spot. Could it be the Grand Canyon?

This was no ordinary place. Others had felt a spiritual connection to the Canyon. It had a long history of indigenous habitation and use. Many tribes considered it sacred ground. In my classes with Red Hawk, he told us of Hopi mythology, wherein man had emerged from the Underworld at Sipapu, a travertine dome with a hole in the top located in the Little Colorado drainage. The spirits of the Hopi dead were also said to return to the Underworld at the same spot. The Paiutes, Hualapai, Havasupai and Navajo also claimed to have significant history in and around the Canyon.

I had assumed my Power Spot would be at a fixed place, not something as immense as this. If it were the Canyon, what did I need to do about it? I didn't really understand the function of a Power Spot. Spirit Dancer had said it was a physical place that would speak to my heart and soul. A place where I'd feel nurtured and where I could renew and reflect. Something was definitely happening. I was in over my head, literally and figuratively. I needed help. It was time for Spirit Dancer to return and straighten this out for me.

A sound that could have been a freight train approaching brought me all the way back to my senses. We were about to run our first rapid, Badger. I remembered seeing it on the colorful maps lining the dining room walls. Now I could hear it, but as I looked downstream, all I could see was what appeared to be a bend in the river. A sharp curve to the right and the river disappeared! I could see Dean's raft in the lead. I watched in horror and fascination as he quickly slid out of view. The other boats followed in quick succession, with the same result. It was like the river swallowed them up, only to spit them out a quarter mile downstream.

Without being able to see the rapid, it was easy for my mind to exaggerate the significance and size of what lay ahead. At the entry, I was relieved to see all the boats right side up. It eased my tension a bit, but I was still in a trainee's boat, and was taking nothing for granted. We slid down what was a silky smooth tongue, and broke through a big wave. James hit them all straight, and we emerged from the rapid wet and smiling. Badger had officially welcomed us to the Grand Canyon. I slid back and did a 'high five' with James.

I looked around, and for the first time I was truly aware of the Canyon rising around me. We had floated only eight miles, but already the imposing walls of sedimentary rock loomed 1,200 feet above us. As we traveled deeper into the earth, I remembered some of my pre-trip reading. We were actually experiencing a journey back in time. We'd begun just prior to the age of the dinosaurs, some 240 million years ago. Each day would find us deeper in the earth and its history, eventually traveling amongst rock almost two billion years old. It was impossible to comprehend, but it would help put much of my life in perspective before we were through.

On that first day, we ran two more significant rapids: Soap Creek at mile 11 and House Rock at mile 17. By mid-afternoon we had covered twenty river miles, and set up camp at a side canyon called North Canyon. With plenty of time before dinner, Greg suggested we take our first hike. I realized that it's one thing to watch the canyon walls rise above you from the river, and it's quite another to walk into geological time as we did on that first hike.

We were in a formation called Supai: a sandstone/limestone/shale combination formed in an ocean environment 320 to 286 million years ago. It was beautiful. For the first time, I noticed the sensuality and feminine nature of the Canyon. Soft curves of hard rock sculpted over time by the forces of nature. I was mesmerized. Hiking in North Canyon was like walking into a sensuous sculpture. The undulating pattern in the rock is caused by a geologic process known as exfoliation. The rock face has been adorned with the rich red-brown pigment of iron oxide that nature supplied from rain and snow melt. As the waters ran over the Hermit Shale layer above the Supai, they mixed with the pigment and painted the rock walls below.

Absorbed with the beauty and not looking where I was going, I almost ran into Jane. She had turned around and was heading back to the boats.

"Isn't this beautiful, Jane. Where are you going?" She mumbled a vague answer about having seen enough and then stared at the ground. I could tell she was frightened over something.

"Don't go back. Greg said there was a beautiful pool up here," I coaxed.

At first I thought she didn't hear and then she slowly turned and we began walking together. At one point we came to a ledge about chest high and looking at Jane, I could see what had intimidated her. Lacing my fingers together, I offered her a step up. Placing one foot in my hand-made stirrup, she made it up and over almost effortlessly. Before long we had caught up to the others. About a half mile up the canyon, we came to a pool of water. We stood for several minutes in reverent silence and awe, feeling our hearts beat, listening to our minds race, watching the world from deep in time, where everything is on purpose and nothing is in a hurry except a lizard eager for a meal. Then, one by one, we held the silence as we headed back to camp.

We were greeted by the mouth-watering aroma of dinner being prepared as we arrived. Rice, grilled haddock, and steamed broccoli, with cherry cobbler for dessert. Another of what would be a long list of pleasant surprises in the Canyon. I hadn't even thought about the quality of the food, and I certainly hadn't expected gourmet. I started calling the guides kitchen magicians for their ability to effortlessly create one taste treat after another.

As we ate dinner, Jane came over to thank me for encouraging her to complete the hike and for helping her get past the ledge. I got to know a little more about her. She was in her late forties, as I had suspected, and from San Francisco. She confessed she had never camped or rafted before.

"Why did you sign up for such a long, rigorous trip if you have never done anything like this," I asked.

"I'm 48 years old and have been taking care of an elderly mother all my adult life. I've watched lots of programs from Walt Disney to Marlin Perkins, and decided I was going to have an adventure at the first opportunity. My mother died a year ago, and after things settled down, I checked in the Sierra Club travel brochure and saw this trip. It fit perfectly into my plans, so I booked it. As soon as I sent in my check, I wondered if I had made a mistake."

"What kind of mistake?" I asked, but I already had a pretty good idea what she would say.

"I've never done anything like this before. I've never traveled alone, never camped in the wilderness, never rafted. I read the brochure, but really had no idea what I was getting into. The more I thought about it, the more nervous I became. But I paid my money, and by God, I was going to do this even if it meant the death of me! And then at Lees Ferry it all came back. I was scared. There were all these questions racing through my head. Questions I'd neglected to ask, about the bathroom facilities, the weather, the critters, even the safety of the guides. I had this strong fear of all the unknowns, and frankly, I was convinced that the worst was right around the next bend. I didn't enjoy the first eight miles because all I could think about was what was going to happen at Badger. I was convinced we were going to flip or smash on a big boulder. I must have been hyper-ventilating when we entered the rapid. I know I was praying mighty hard."

"Must have been a real relief when you made it through safely."

"Oh my yes! I wanted to sing hallelujah, but I was too embarrassed. I've learned so much already, Charly. After running those three rapids today, I realize my fear was from ignorance. It wasn't fear of the unknown. It was actually fear of the 'known', what I 'knew' would happen because I had seen *Deliverance*, and some of my friends had told me I was downright crazy to be doing this. I allowed that to influence me."

She reached over and squeezed my hand as she continued. "But now that I've made it through today, I realize how buoyant the rafts are, and how good the guides are. Dean told us today that a boat can flip in any rapid, and I believe him. But I realize now it's not likely. I heard that Marian has made 75 trips down here and hasn't flipped yet. Those are pretty good odds. I'm actually looking forward to the Roaring Twenties tomorrow, and I might even sit in the front." She had a smile on her face that said more than any words possibly could.

Brave woman, I thought to myself. "Takes a lot of courage to do what you're doing," I told her. "If you ever need help it would be an honor to provide it if I can."

"You've already helped me more than you will ever know," she replied in a very serious tone. "I was on my way back to the boats when you encouraged me to turn around. If you hadn't done that and helped me over that ledge, I would have missed some incredible beauty. I've been so busy helping others that I forgot myself. That's why I'm on this trip. As scary as it is, I want to do it."

She let go of my hand, "How did you feel, Charly, when you were at Lees Ferry waiting for the trip to begin?"

"To tell you the truth, I just wanted to get going. I've already done two river trips in Utah, and I figured this would be pretty much the same. It's already obvious this trip will be way different." My voice trailed off and tears formed in my eyes as I recalled the sensations and emotions of the morning.

"I know I won't be the same person when I leave here."

Chapter Six

The Real
Journey
Begins

There is a very compelling feeling in the Canyon, especially around sunset and dusk. That first night we were all treated to an extraordinary color exhibition which is common in the Canyon. When the sun is close to the horizon, at sunrise and sunset, only the long rays of the spectrum, the reds and oranges, make it through our atmosphere. The dance of these colors on the sedimentary rock layers, now soaring 1,800 feet above us, reflected a dazzling display of reds, oranges, and golds. Their brilliance took our breath away.

I was surprised at how early darkness arrived at North Canyon. Soon after the light show faded, the colors receded from view and the shadows descended. Our focus at dusk was in stark contrast to the light show that preceded it. Sunset on the canyon walls commanded our attention. The deepening shadows of approaching night invited me to journey inward, where I had the opportunity to reflect upon the day and the trip so far.

This was new for me. Like many others, I had been caught up in the "doing of life." Doing work, doing relationships, doing play, doing health. I'd never taken time to look inside and meet myself, maybe because I was afraid of what I would find. As I lay there on the beach, Vega and Arcturus, and then lesser magnitude stars appeared above me, and that reality jolted me. Like Jane, I had spent my whole life wanting to be liked and accepted by others. The best way to accomplish that, I had concluded, was to please them. As a result, my whole being was focused on what others wanted, instead of what I wanted and needed. I felt a tear slide down my right temple as a deep sadness swelled in my chest. The feeling was familiar, as if it had been my companion for a long time. I realized I had become so good at coping with my disappointments that I wasn't even aware of how I stuffed my feelings. When I experienced disappointments, I would think, "Oh well, next time," or "This too shall pass."

My mind told me I shouldn't be feeling these emotions. After all, I was in the Grand Canyon, on a trip I'd anticipated for so long. It had been a great day, why spoil it with stupid feelings that I couldn't do anything about anyway. Spilt milk and all that. I couldn't shake the feelings even though they scared me. Tears flowed. It felt bad, it felt good. I was confused.

"You are listening to your heart, Charly. It is an important and courageous thing to do."

It was Spirit Dancer. Her soft voice came as a pleasant surprise. I could see her plainly. Her white deerskin robe glowed. Jane's tent was only about thirty feet away, and I looked around to see if she could see Spirit Dancer too. Jane was intent on reading outside her tent, in full view, but she wasn't noticing anything in my direction. Several others were still standing around the cooking stoves. No one paid any attention.

"Tears are the Great Spirit's gift for cleansing, Charly. Do not be afraid. They help remove toxins and facilitate healing. Be with yourself in this moment and just feel. Don't think, do nothing. Just be aware of yourself, of your heart, and feel your sadness. I will be here and when you are ready, I will speak again."

I felt a sense of comfort knowing she was present. So I lay there and did as she said. I lost track of time. At some point I looked over at her and I heard myself asking, "What are these tears about? I just had one of the best days I can remember. This whole experience is so weird. And, I feel like I've been here before, but of course I haven't. What's going on?" I sat up cross-legged and looked at her.

"You have been reconnected with your Power Spot, Charly." Spirit Dancer's voice was like a mother's touch on a fevered brow. "Indeed, you have been here before. Yahoo painted this in your Book of Life. It's been inside your box all this time. Because it is familiar, you are more comfortable being yourself. The tears are both joy and sadness. The joy is for coming home. You have never really felt at home anywhere, have you?"

"No. I guess not." I thought about it for a minute. "Even though I love my family, I always felt out of place, like I never fit in. What is the sadness about?"

"You tell me."

"I don't know," I answered quickly. I wanted her to just tell me.

"That's a lie. You may think you don't know, but that's because you aren't completely in touch with your feelings. Let's look back at the Puzzle Theory. You have been living according to the picture on the outside of your box, the one you were taught to believe is true. It has been so long since you knew who you really are, that you think and behave as who you are not. Of course, that is understandable, because you can't know who you are if you don't know who you are not."

"Spirit Dancer, sometimes you talk in circles. Do you mean my sadness is for not living my life my way?"

"Yes, but it's more for the recognition that you have not given yourself permission to feel and be who you really are. Your need for approval has been so strong that you disconnected from your truth and put your attention on what you thought other people wanted from you. So your decisions were not your truth. And they were not anyone else's truth either."

"Not anyone else's truth?" I was lost.

"You were guessing what others might want from you when you chose your behavior. You can never know what another is think-ing or wanting. Sometimes you were right, but other times your guesses were off the mark. Your choices were always based on your own needs. And your actions were always unclean."

"What do you mean, unclean?" I was becoming defensive. I changed positions, suddenly feeling uncomfortable all over.

"Think of your actions as giving a gift. A true gift is some-thing you want to give, to someone who wants to receive it, with no strings attached. How many of your actions were true gifts?"

I didn't have to think very long. "Based on that definition, not many, I'm ashamed to say."

"Charly, don't be so hard on yourself. Your intentions were good, but you weren't serving yourself. This is not about right or wrong, but it is about consequences. How many times have you said 'yes' to someone out of a sense of obligation or neediness?"

"Too often," I replied, again I didn't have to think very long. I wanted to change the subject.

"It would be useful for you to remember this lesson about obligation. It helps no one. So the next time you feel obligation coming on, lie down until it passes." She smiled and I couldn't help but smile.

"If I did that, I'd be in the prone position much of the time. I'd never get anything accomplished." I almost laughed.

"You aren't getting much accomplished now, Charly. Your life is unproductive precisely because you are spending most of your time waiting for others to live it for you. You ask your friends to take care of you, you want your business partner to make you successful, your lovers to make you feel good. Aren't you tired of waiting for others to rescue you?"

"Oh God, yes. But if I don't do things for people when they ask, then I'll really be alone."

"Good," she said matter-of-factly.

"Good? What's good about it. I'm tired of being alone. I want to share my life with a special woman. I want to have a best friend I can hang with. I've already done too much by myself." All my pent-up frustration came rushing out.

Spirit Dancer was ever patient, and the opal heart in the eagle flashed. "First, you are never alone. Second, no one wants you to do anything out of a sense of obligation, and that is how you've been giving your gifts. For example, there are lots of ways you say 'yes' when you would prefer to say 'no.'"

"What do you mean?" I asked, defensive again.

"In response to a request you say, 'I suppose so,' or 'I'll try,' or 'I'll see if I can make it.' In truth those are all 'no' and most people sense this and feel uneasy with your answer. They don't want your obligation. So, if you really want to develop powerful relationships, begin by telling the truth. If you can't say absolutely 'yes' then say 'no.' Your friends and family will respect your honesty. Understand the focus here is being truthful with yourself, which is really saying 'yes' to the world."

"Phew, that's a tall order. But it sure makes sense. It's not going to be easy changing habits of a lifetime, but you didn't say this journey would be easy. It feels real scary, because everything in me says no one will like me, and I'll be alone for the rest of my life." Those thoughts almost put me into a panic.

"I understand the fear, most humans have it. There is a big difference between being alone and feeling lonely. You are opening up to your spirituality. Connecting with the Great Spirit will guarantee you will never be alone. In order to realize your connection to the Everything, you must first come into relationship with yourself. No one can accomplish this for you. This is not something you can ask your friends to help with. That is why you are here, not only in the Grand Canyon, but also in this body at this time. The first step in deepening your relationship with yourself is to get to know you. That's why it would be good to be alone, you'll have fewer distractions."

I understood what she was saying, but the fear of loneliness was strong.

She continued, "Charly, what you see in the outer world is merely a reflection of your inner consciousness. It is feedback to let you know how you are doing. Change your life within, and you will change what you experience without. It is a Natural Law. First within, then without. You have said you want freedom. To achieve it, you must first stand in your own circle. Your soul has only one purpose, and that is to discover and express who you are."

I could feel a rising anxiety in my gut. "But I don't know who I am. And I don't know how to find out."

"This is your quest, to find out. But, it is not true that you don't know who you are. You just think you don't know. It is all within you, within your box. Yahoo put it there, and your purpose for being on this raft journey is for you to discover who you really are."

"I have lived 35 years as somebody else. I'm not going to get rid of all that in two weeks." I said, both exasperated and scared that what I just said might be true.

"You have the rest of your life, and more, to do this. It is not important how long this takes. Worrying will interfere with your exploration. You will take what time you need. You are an explorer seeking to discover who you are, one piece of the puzzle at a time. This can be a very enjoyable experience. The only way to lose that joy is to place some unreasonable expectations on yourself. Have you ever been hitchhiking?"

"Yes, many times," I turned and looked directly at her wondering where she was going with this.

"Did you enjoy it?"

"Most of the time," I replied.

"When did you not enjoy it?"

I thought for a minute, "When I was pressed for time.....Aha! I see what you mean. I loved hitchhiking, being out in the country, wondering who I would meet, how far we would journey together, what I would learn about myself and others. The only time I hated it was when I had to be somewhere at a certain time. I would actually take it personally when no one would stop. Imagine that. People didn't know me, but I would be angry at them for not stopping. It was the time factor."

"Exactly. When time is not an issue you are able to be in the here and now, which is actually the only place and only time you can be. Now, are you ready to continue your exploration?" she said.

"But I don't even know how to get started." I replied, sounding like a scared little boy. I stopped talking, took a deep breath thinking, "Oh, what the hell. What have I got to lose?"

"Your pain, for one thing," Spirit Dancer chimed in. I was startled, she had read my thoughts. I looked around again. Jane was still reading. My thoughts returned to our conversation.

"Good point. OK, let's go for it!" I said.

She nodded and lifted her hands palms outward and looked off in the distance. "As I have said, all the answers you seek are already present, but you may have trouble recognizing this. The key to some of your answers will be found in the world around you."

"Interesting," I said, "and what exactly does that mean?"

"If you want to improve the quality of your life, you must be conscious all the time. This is also known as being mindful. Be a powerful observer of what goes on in the world: the actions of people, so-called coincidences, things that happen in nature. This includes your inner world of thoughts, instincts, and emotions. While you are on this trip, you will learn about yourself by observing your fellow passengers and the guides; by noticing the natural world; and by paying attention to your own experiences."

I acknowledged, and she went on.

"You also need to understand that the greatest gift you can give yourself is to accept personal responsibility for your choices and your outcomes. By doing this, you become accountable to yourself. You will no longer be at the mercy of any person or thing, any experience or circumstance. When you embrace yourself, you take a giant step towards the true freedom you seek."

"Can you say more about that?" I'd always thought I was responsible.

"Just this. Humans believe who they are is what they do. What you do and how you do it are only manifestations of who you are. In spite of what you have come to believe, you are not what you do, nor are you what you wear, what you eat, how your body looks, or any of the other external measurements humans use to judge themselves and others. Since all of those ingredients are subject to personal interpretation, you have no control over how people will perceive you. So it would be wise for you to remember the following:

> It doesn't matter what you do
> until you accept yourself.
> Once you accept yourself,
> it doesn't matter what you do."

"Look, I understand most of what you just said. But I need some help with the 'observing others' piece. How do I get to know me better by watching what others do?"

Now she thought for a moment. "By not leaving what you observe 'out there.'"

"Say what?" She was too far "out there" for me.

"Charly, never leave what you see in the external world out there. You have to bring it back to yourself. If you admire something you see in someone else, it is a quality you possess and wish to develop. If you judge something about someone else, it has something to do with you. For example, what did you learn about yourself through your experience today with Jane?"

"I don't see how that relates to me. That was her experience." I knew I was fighting this.

Spirit Dancer seemed to have all the patience and time in the world. "There are two ways for you to gain insight into who you are through others. First, what do you notice about them? Second, what do you notice about yourself in your interaction with them? What you notice about them can be a reflection for you. It's not people's actions that speak to you about you, it's how you perceive them. What did you notice about Jane?"

"Well, she's gentle, gutsy, has more capability than she realizes." I paused, "Is trying to do things alone, has spent her life taking care of . . . " I paused again. "I'm beginning to see what you mean. So what I see in others are really aspects of me, that I'm seeing in them. I'm seeing my own gentleness, courage, potential, as well as the lone wolf and caretaker?"

"You've got the idea. This can be a little tricky. This holds for what you like, as well as what you don't like. In general, what you see in others that draws your attention says something about you. So if you see courage in someone else and you feel a warm glow, that says something about your own courage. If you see anger in someone else and you want to run away, that says something about your own anger and your fear. Pay attention to what you see in the world. If it gets your attention, bring it back to you. You wouldn't recognize it if it wasn't within you. Now, what about your interaction with Jane?"

"I don't follow, what do you mean?" I questioned.

"What did you do that felt good? What did you notice about you as a result of what you did? How did you feel when she was describing her experiences?"

I was having to dig deep. "Oh, I see what you're getting at. Well, it felt good to speak to her and encourage her to go back in. I really enjoyed helping her over that ledge. It seemed like she was walking more lightly after that, and it makes me smile just thinking about it. I also was surprised at how important she thought my role was. It didn't seem like much to me."

Spirit Dancer looked pleased. "Excellent. Now, what does all that say about who you are?"

I paused, then replied, "When I first spoke to Jane, I had no reason to believe anything was wrong. It was just a gut instinct. It was risky to speak up, because she might have been embarrassed or angry at me. So that says I'm courageous, that I am somewhat intuitive, and that I care about others. I certainly didn't help out of obligation today. How's that?"

She nodded, "A good start. What else?"

She wanted more. "I like to help people, particularly to help them help themselves. I believed she could do more than she thought she could, which must mean I can do more than I think I can. I care about myself, am capable of doing a lot, and I downplay my impact on others. The fact is, I'm a very capable, powerful man who has the confidence to help others. Wow! This is exciting! I never thought anything through like this before."

"You're a quick study." Holding up a finger, she added, "One word of caution. The purpose of your observing others is to deepen your relationships. Never take yourself or your tyrants too seriously."

"What do you mean, tyrants," I inquired, stifling a yawn. I had just about had it.

She saw my yawn, "It's late. We'll end for now. Pay attention to everything that goes on around you, and within you. You'll know when it's time to learn about tyrants. Pleasant dreams, Charly. You've come a long way today. Continue to feel the energy, and notice, just notice."

I was still wondering what kind of tyrants would be on a rafting trip, when Spirit Dancer rose and began walking down the river. As she walked, the robe swayed and I was sure I could hear the necklace jingle. The image dimmed. I glanced around and North Canyon was silent. I laid back on my pillow just in time to watch a spectacular shooting star blaze across the Canyon, as if connecting one side with the other. It was curious timing, and I started to think about its significance, but my eyes were too heavy to think for long.

Chapter Seven

No
Accidental
Coincidences

I was in a deep sleep when the first conch shell sounded, dragging the caffeine deprived out of their bags. It was an ethereal sound, and at first I lay there wondering where on earth I was. Then I remembered I was finally on my long-awaited trip. I smiled, as I remembered Dean telling me of the ritual "blowing of the conch shell". Since I don't drink coffee, I lay in my sleeping bag a few moments longer. My eyes were drawn to the canyon walls that rose above our camp. The sun was once again adding its artists touch to the rock pallet. This time gold was the pigment of choice and as I watched the color slip down the canyon walls I thought about one of my favorite songs which referred to the early sun burning golden on the mountain, and the feeling of freedom personified in a soaring eagle.

A warm feeling of well-being and freedom rose from my toes and permeated my body. After only one day I was more comfortable in this harsh wilderness than I ever felt at home in Michigan.

Spirit Dancer had said my task was to observe and see what I could learn about myself. Because I was so impressed by the morning colors, I concluded that I, too, must be a colorful person. Interesting thought, because I was basically a very shy person.

I joined the others and wondered if anyone might mention they had seen me talking to a strange woman in white last night. But no one said a thing. Breakfast was delicious. I decided everything must taste good in the Grand Canyon. Maybe there was pixie dust in the air too. I had already felt the magic.

As we ate, Greg gave us a run down of what we'd be encountering on the river today. Funny, Greg was really a quiet, unassuming sort of guy, but the crew certainly seemed to have a great deal of respect for him. I'd always thought leaders needed to be charismatic and vocal, so it would be very interesting to get to know Greg and find out how he pulled it off. I decided to ride on his boat today. Maybe I'd get some insight.

We all pitched in, cleaned up and loaded the boats. With everyone anticipating the Roaring Twenties, a series of medium sized rapids in close proximity to each other, no one seemed to notice the billowy cumulo-nimbus clouds building just downstream and moving in our direction.

I said good-bye to North Canyon wondering if all the camps would be so incredible. Jane and Richard had also piled into Greg's raft. Richard was a jovial guy, but definitely 40 to 50 pounds overweight. He seemed a little self-conscious, joking about how he might sink the raft as he climbed in. We all laughed and the day was off to a good start. There was a small rapid just below camp which got me immediately into a river mood. The water felt particularly cold first thing in the morning, but it guaranteed that everyone would be wide awake when we ran the bigger rapids. Richard, sitting in the front, had gotten especially soaked by a good wave.

None of us were paying attention when thunder announced the incoming storm. It seemed to appear without warning. An upstream wind preceded heavy rain. I turned around and watched the other boats. The wind was so strong that all the guides were straining just to keep their rafts in the current and moving downstream. Then my attention was drawn to Greg. I was amazed at how calm he seemed to be in the midst of this sudden, unexpected turmoil, and impressed with how effortless his movements were. His rowing was smooth and consistent. His face showed no strain. In fact it betrayed a very subtle, but unmistakable smile.

At first, the other passengers grumbled about the storm. They had come for fun in the sun, and here they were getting pummeled by sheets of wind-blown rain. Fortunately, most had donned their rain gear as protection from the cold river water that Greg had warned us about, so no one was really suffering. Greg remained calm and steady, and now that the wind was dying down, some of the other guides seemed to be enjoying the storm in spite of the strain.

I heard Wally yell, "Look for waterfalls! If this lasts long enough we should see some spectacular ones in this part of the Canyon!" I remembered that Wally was the guide studying biology at Northern Arizona. The thought struck me that if I hung around him, I could probably learn a lot about nature on this trip.

Pretty soon everybody forgot that this wasn't their idea of perfect weather, and they began getting into the spirit. When waterfalls started appearing, we all were hooting and hollering. What a sight! They were everywhere. I was amazed at how they formed. First I could see one beginning 1,500 feet above us, and then the water would drop into some plateau and disappear. Five minutes later, it would reappear at the next level, and then the next, until finally it would plunge into the Colorado, turning it into a red-brown soup.

I commented on the color of the water to Richard. Greg overheard and said, "This is how the river looked all the time, before they dammed it up. Rio Colorado, the Spanish name for the river, means river that runs red." I remembered reading about all the controversy surrounding the building of Glen Canyon Dam upstream. It was the dam that created Lake Powell, part of the Glen Canyon Recreation Area in Utah. There still seemed to be some debate as to whether the dam was necessary at all.

The storm was short lived. Within an hour it had blasted through and the sun was upon us. Everybody was energized, and Greg remained steadfast and silent. As the morning progressed it was evident we all respected this quiet giant. If you wanted to be in a safe boat, Greg's would do very well, thank you.

After running the Roaring Twenties, the river became very mellow. I thought back remembering my evenings with Dean and the maps on the dining room wall. We were now in the early layers of Redwall Limestone, named for the reddish pigment that had washed down from the Hermit Shale two layers above, leaving a red veneer coating. We were in a segment of Grand Canyon called Marble Canyon, so named by Major John Wesley Powell during his first exploration of the Canyon in 1869. He named it Marble Canyon because the limestone, when polished and sculpted by the sediment filled river, reminded him of marble, which is actually metamorphosed limestone.

Here the walls rose straight out of the river, and I sensed how deep we were in the Canyon. At one point we stopped to fill our water bottles and jugs with fresh water flowing out of the limestone wall.

Greg told us to keep our eyes pealed. Just downstream was a large eroded cave known as Redwall Cavern. When it came into view I was amazed. Carved by flash floods that roared through the Canyon each spring, it was a gigantic place, and we all felt dwarfed by it. The sheer wall directly across from the cavern seemed to focus the energy into the cavern itself. When Greg told us they had a string quartet concert there every year, I could only imagine how amazing it would be to lie on the silky sand listening to Mozart.

Leaving Redwall Cavern, our camp for the night was only eight miles away. The river was mellow, so Greg offered to let me row. The oars felt natural in my hands and I felt somehow different, larger, rowing the raft in this incredible place. I started to feel very confident, imagining what it would be like to work as a commercial guide. Of course, I hadn't even run a rapid yet, but hey, how hard could it be? Greg made it look so easy.

Rounding a bend I could hear a low growling sound being carried upstream by a soft breeze. "What's that?" I inquired, a small butterfly appearing in my gut.

"Thirty-six mile," Greg replied matter-of-factly. "Want to run it?"

I hesitated. "Sure," I replied, hoping he couldn't hear my uncertainty. "What do I do?"

"Well, it's a relatively short rapid with a little right to left bend halfway through," Greg said simply.

I couldn't see a thing. There was a slight drop at the beginning, obscuring part of the rapid from my sight.

"OK," he said, "go down the tongue, give a push for momentum as you hit the waves, and keep the raft straight. You shouldn't have any problem."

"Easy for you to say," I thought as I swallowed hard. All of a sudden I could feel moistness in my palms as I tightly gripped the oars.

We entered and made it through the first few waves, and I remember saying, "This is a piece of cake." Just then a wave came from the right and lifted the boat sideways.

"High side!" shouted Greg as he threw all his weight into the right tube. Jane and Richard followed suit. It seemed to work, because the raft settled back and continued downstream as if nothing had happened.

I was shaking and my heart was pounding. "What happened?" I asked, feeling both embarrassed and chastened for thinking I was better than I was.

"No big deal," Greg reassured me. "Can't take anything for granted down here. As soon as you think you're in control, the river will let you know who really is. Don't worry, you're doing fine."

Jane piped up, "Yeah, you did great Charly." Richard gave me the "OK" sign.

I appreciated their words of support, but felt very self conscious and decided to go back to being a passenger again. For the rest of the float to camp, I barely noticed the Canyon. As spectacular as it was, I was still back at thirty-six mile wishing I could do it over again.

The activity at camp, a place called Buck Farm at mile 41, helped keep my mind off my afternoon folly. I was on the cooking crew and there was a lot to do, rinsing and cutting the vegetables, pumping fresh water, responding to requests that were more like orders. The rest of the crew didn't have time to train me, so I had to learn as quickly as possible.

After dinner, I decided I needed to get off by myself and explore a little. It wasn't quite sundown so I figured I had some time. I found a trail leading toward the side canyon behind camp and followed it. In no time I was out of sight and sound of the river, walking in silence that was so strong I resented the noise from my shoes. On the first hike, the day before, I was always with people and couldn't hear the silence. Here it was almost deafening.

At first the canyon seemed dry, just a lot of boulders lying over, under and around each other. I imagined them creating shelters and playgrounds for the "little people" who must inhabit such a place. I was convinced the entire Canyon was magic by now. Water began appearing as trickles emerging from the limestone rock layers. Where there is water there is life, and what had been arid and lifeless now became lush, and green. It was like a gift from the desert and spoke of the persistence of life in a seemingly lifeless place.

I continued on and found myself in a huge amphitheater. The canyon continued, but I was held by this place. In the center was a very large cottonwood tree, perhaps 100 feet or taller. The walls seemed to arch in as they rose high above me, and something told me to find a comfortable spot and stay awhile.

I climbed the convenient stair steps of the Muav limestone and found a place with some soft vegetation where I could sit. Folding my legs under me, I took several deep breaths and absorbed all my eyes could capture. Then I closed them and listened to the silence, to my breathing, to the Canyon Wren and his descending musical trill, and to the voice of the spotted Canyon Frog echoing off the walls. I was surprised at how closely it resembled the bleating of a Big Horn sheep.

Subtly and ever so softly I heard Spirit Dancer's voice in my head. I opened my eyes and saw her sitting on a boulder a short distance away.

"Do you know any more about who you are, Charly?'

"I thought this was going to be a vacation," I blurted out.

"Am I going to have to work the entire trip? I was just enjoying the silence." The afternoon embarrassment of almost flipping the raft was still with me, and I was sure Spirit Dancer was going to comment on it.

"Freedom comes with a price, Charly. You volunteered for this journey, and you determine when and how much you will work. I drew you to this spot because I knew it would calm you. There are many I am guiding. If you'd prefer, I'll find one who is ready." It looked as if she was going to leave.

"No, wait! I'm just enjoying this peaceful feeling. Especially after that mess I made of things today." I said rather contritely.

"That was no mess. But it was a great lesson." She had a smile on her face.

"You don't have to make fun of me," I replied defensively. "It was embarrassing enough this afternoon."

"What was embarrassing about it?" Spirit Dancer asked softly.

"What was embarrassing?!! I almost flipped the raft in a nothing rapid, that's what was so embarrassing! I can just see it now. He flipped in the first rapid he ever rowed. Ended his career right then and there." I said, disgustedly.

"Self pity is so unbecoming, Charly. It would be better if you benefited from the experience. This is not the way to do that." As ever, her patience was endless.

"OK, so how can I do that?" I asked rather pointedly.

"By valuing your mistake and being willing to learn from it. What was going on just before you made the so-called mistake?" she queried.

"I was in a great space. I felt right at home on the oars, was even fantasizing about being a raft guide. It all felt so natural, you know?"

She nodded. "I do. Then what happened?"

"I heard the rapid before I saw it and got a little nervous. Then we rounded the bend and I saw it, and it sounded even louder and I got scared."

"Did you tell anyone how you were feeling?" Still patient.

"Are you kidding?! That wouldn't be cool. No way. Why?" I couldn't believe she'd ask a question like that.

"Its natural to be a bit fearful when you're feeling out of control. This was your first rapid, no one expected you to be a seasoned guide. If you had just acknowledged your fear, you would have been much more present, and you probably would have noticed the wave that almost flipped your boat. And what was it you said just before that happened?" She tilted her head slightly forward and her long hair fell off her shoulder.

I was annoyed and starting to feel even more stupid. "I don't remember. What difference does it make anyway?"

"Accepting yourself and taking personal responsibility is the difference. What you did was bring out the 'macho male' in you. 'Piece of cake' was what I believe you said, am I correct?"

"Yeah," I admitted rather sheepishly.

"You were covering up your nervousness because you didn't want anyone to know you were afraid. The result was you received a reminder from the river as to who is really in charge. You will find that the natural world is a perfect reflection of your state of mind, and you will receive what I call 'immediate performance appraisal.' In a very real sense, the river heard you boast you were in control and gave you a quick lesson. You would be best to remain aware of it."

"I see what you mean. So it wasn't just a coincidence that wave showed up right after I said that?" I raised my eyebrows as I looked at her.

"There are no accidental coincidences, just meaningful ones. You can ignore them if you wish, but you will keep getting them until you learn the lesson. Remember that advertisement on television a few years back, about changing your oil?"

I had to think for a minute. "You mean the one about the defenseless woman driving alone on a dark back road with a sinister hitchhiker waiting to do her great bodily harm?"

"That's the one. What was the punch line, Charly?"

"Let's see. Oh yeah, I remember. Pay me now or pay me later." She had made her point.

"Bingo. So you can pay now, as you did today, and learn. Or

you can pay later. One thing you should know about all this, however." She paused, waiting.

"What's that?" I asked, not sure I wanted to know.

"The Universe has a way of raising the volume for those who don't seem to be listening. So the next time, it may not be a near miss. Do you want to take that chance?"

"No." Today was enough, I reckoned.

"Then what were the lessons from today?"

She had made a good point, so I thought about it for a few moments. "First, don't take the river for granted. There is a way to get through rapids relatively easily, but I won't find it if I don't respect its power. Its like I need to work with the river, not against it. Greg went through those rapids today like a hot knife through butter. It was like he and the river were in a partnership. He found the right path and the river carried us through. In my case, it was like I was in a competition with the river."

"Very true." Spirit Dancer interjected. "You chose to be separate from the river rather than a part of it. A raindrop becomes part of the river, but is no less important because of it. Raindrops have no ego, humans do. You are driven to control everything. Down here you will learn to go with the flow or pay the price. What else?"

"In line with what you just said, a little humility would go a long way. I don't have to be the hero. Fact is, I am blessed with excellent physical abilities. I don't need to impress others with my prowess. I'm struck by how silent the river is, yet how powerful. Perhaps that's a good reminder to all of us to be more quiet about who we are. I think Greg understands this."

She was silent, so I went on. "Third, if I'm willing to learn from my mistakes, I won't have to make so many. Right? Fourth, I really love this place, and I should pay attention to that."

"Excellent," said Spirit Dancer agreeing. "Let me add something to your last point. Too few people follow their heart. That is one of the main causes of the burnout you see all around you. Have you noticed how demanding the guide's job is?"

"Yes. And yet the guides seem so energized when they're

here. They work so well together, and do everything so willingly and joyfully," I added.

"True. There are very few jobs that require as much effort, physically, mentally or emotionally, as this one. Rarely do you see people working this hard with this much enthusiasm. It is because they love what they do, and they are driven to share the experience with others."

She thought for a second. "This would be a good time to share some Native American wisdom with you. It has to do with the heart. There is a proper choreography, or pattern, for receiving, processing, and giving out information. It goes like this:

> *Receive with the Mind,*
> *Hold with the Body,*
> *Determine with the Spirit,*
> *Give with the Heart.*"

I sat thinking and she continued.

"The normal pattern is to 'receive with the heart' and 'give with the mind.' Another term for this is called 'judgment.' Pay attention to what is in your heart that you can give out. It is what your soul wishes for you. What else did you learn today? What did you notice about Greg?"

Ahh . . . Greg. I had paid attention to Greg. "He doesn't say much. Doesn't have to. His actions speak volumes about his confidence and his competence. I was amazed at how effortlessly he rowed, even during the storm when all the other guides were really straining. He didn't seem to work any harder. He seemed so calm and relaxed, I'm sure everyone is going to want to be in his boat when we get to the really big water."

I paused, thinking, and then went on. "I also noticed how upset people were when the storm surprised us. Some told me later they were regretting their decision to be here. But then we all got into it."

"What caused the shift?" asked Spirit Dancer.

"The guides. They were so charged, so into the lightning and thunder. Even Greg had a smile on his face. And then the waterfalls were so spectacular. How could we not get excited."

"So, what caused the shift? It was a shift, wasn't it?"

Spirit Dancer smiled at my determination. "We saw another way to look at the storm. Instead of what it was taking from us, sun, the clear river, warmth, we became open to the adventure of being part of a powerful natural occurrence. All the things that happened, the waterfalls, the river changing color, the lightning and thunder, how the Canyon felt and smelled, added to the trip."

"Right. You just walked around the Wheel." She said.

"The Wheel? There are no wheels down here. Oh, you must mean a Medicine Wheel." I was warming to this, and I leaned back on my elbows.

Spirit Dancer began. "Do you remember the teachings from your friend Red Hawk of years ago?"

"Some," I nodded.

"Native peoples use the shield, or the wheel, as both a teaching and a learning symbol. In your world, the triangle is the most obvious symbol. Your corporations broadcast their organization charts which are hierarchical in nature. Your schools set up reward systems to benefit the top 10% in academics and athletics. Social circles usually have people who carry more weight."

"Right," I added.

"With a wheel there is no hierarchy. I want you to do something. Pick out small, loose pebbles, being sure not to disturb anything that is fixed in place, and form a small circle. Then find any object and put it in the center of the circle." She motioned, pointing to the clear spot in front of me.

I created the circle and found a leaf that had fallen from a nearby redbud tree and did as she instructed.

When I was done, she continued. "Notice no place on this circle is any more important than any other place. Each place does, however, represent a different viewing point."

"What does that mean, different viewing point," I asked.

"Look at the leaf from straight above it. Now look at it from the east on the Wheel, or the right side. Now look at it from the south, or below it."

I did as she instructed

"What did you notice?"

"I could see the entire leaf from above, only the curved section from the right, and it looked totally different from the bottom." It was something I'd never done before.

"It looks different from every place on the Wheel, yet it is the same object. The same is true of circumstances, as you saw today with the storm, and with people and beliefs, and so on. By the way, you didn't see the entire leaf from above. You only saw the exposed half. There is still the underside and all that is inside, including parts we can't see with the naked eye. There is so much more to everything than what we think. You're familiar with the term illusion, are you not?" she questioned.

"Of course." I said.

She stood, moved forward, and pointed at the Wheel I'd drawn. "Illusion is defined as believing in only one viewpoint rather than knowing there are multiple viewing points for everything. You walked around the Wheel this morning. It allowed you to see the same experience from a different direction, a different viewing point. That's how you shift your perspective. Life is a perceptual experience, Charly. Who do you think chooses the perception?"

Now she was looking at me. "I do. So....I'm getting it! So it's not what happens to me that's important; it's really what I do with it that counts, right?" I felt like a little kid who had just found an extra candy bar I could have all to myself.

"Gold star for you, Charly. This is how you move toward more freedom. Take responsibility for your choices, how you perceive your experiences, and the outcomes you get. It leads to self acceptance, because you are no longer at the mercy of anyone or anything. You don't need others to tell you you're OK. You know it for yourself, regardless of what others think." She sat back down on the boulder and pulled the deerskin around her.

"Still sounds like a lot of work." When I felt like this, I knew I was getting tired. Events of the day were wearing on me.

"It is, and it gets easier. It's like any learning curve. You start out being totally unconscious. You don't have a clue, and you're not even aware that you don't have a clue. It's actually a painful place to be in, but you don't realize it, and the pain is so subtle you think it's normal, which it is. Some people call this the place of unconscious incompetence. Then you come to a place where you don't have a clue, but you realize you don't, conscious incompetence. It's both painful and exciting, because when you start to wake up, you then have choices. You can do something to change your circumstances whereas previously you didn't think you had any control over them."

I agreed.

"Then you arrive at having a clue, and knowing it. Some people call this conscious competence. You know and you know you know. Finally you know so well that you don't even think about it any more."

"Great. I want to be there." I was ready for anything that sounded like the end of the journey, right now.

"You will. But you won't remain there long." She added.

"But why not? Why wouldn't I want to be there? It would make life so easy."

"Life was not meant to be easy, or comfortable, or painless, Charly. Remember the Cycle of Living? 'Death gives life, Life gives rebirth' With each death of an aspect of who you are not, you reveal and can express more of who you are. You also develop greater awareness of who you are not, because you know when an action or a thought, or a belief, feels right and when it doesn't. In a very real way, living life as an adventure requires you to consistently place yourself at the low end of the learning curve."

I was deep in thought. She continued. "Perhaps this will help. Think of yourself as an explorer, seeking to discover how the puzzle pieces in your box fit together. Your focus is on the exploration and the discovery of your vision. You know what you are seeking, and you have the tools to determine when you have found it. Nothing else matters. If you want to play it safe, if you need comfort, then you will not succeed."

I jumped on that one. "Wait a minute, what's wrong with comfort?"

"Nothing is wrong with it, Charly. But seeking comfort means not taking risks. Explorers are risk takers who must go outside their comfort zone to make their discoveries. Gandhi would not have made the difference he made had he been motivated to seek comfort. Mother Teresa could not have accomplished so much if she had insisted on a comfortable life. You are exploring who you are after living somebody else's version of your life. To succeed in this discovery, you have to push the boundaries of what's possible. If you want comfort, you won't do what it takes."

"But what if I get lost? What if I don't know how to get where I want to go?" I was overwhelmed again.

"There will be times when you will feel lost. All you need do is walk around the Wheel and look at things from a different viewing point." Again she indicated the circle at my feet.

"For instance?" I asked

"You won't be lost if you have a vision of what you are seeking. It's true you won't always know how you're going to get where you're going. Focus on the vision, it will be the magnet that keeps you moving ahead, piece by piece. It has its challenges, of course, but the more conscious you are about where you are, the more competent you will be about accelerating your learning curve. I think you'll find it actually becomes quite enjoyable."

"I'll take your word for it. At this point it appears daunting, to say the least. But I am beginning to understand what you are saying." I suddenly looked around. I had been so focused on my conversation with Spirit Dancer, I hadn't noticed that darkness had descended. I was horrified.

"Oh my God, it's dark!" I proclaimed as if it was a blinding flash of the obvious.

"So it is," Spirit Dancer remarked, seeing nothing unusual about it.

"How am I going to get back to camp? I have no flashlight?"

"Charly, you are here in the Canyon to help in your commitment to have more freedom in your life. There is more, much more to it than I have told you."

I didn't need any more lessons tonight. All I could think of was getting back to camp. "Great, just what I wanted to hear. But what does that have to do with me getting back to camp in one piece." I could see stars, but no moon to light the way.

She was actually smiling, and it annoyed me. "I have told you this trip is about deepening your relationship with yourself. Discovering more of who you are. But that is only one aspect of your assignment. The Canyon will also be helpful in three other primary areas for you to explore in more depth later. But only after you have reached the crux in your relationship with yourself."

"What do you mean, crux?" I interrupted. "What is a crux and how will I know I've reached it?" I hoped it had something to do with me seeing in the dark.

The darkness wasn't phasing her. She still had a lesson for me. "Good question. Glad you asked. Yesterday Jane came to a crux, the ledge. It was the point at which you can move ahead with more certainty and confidence, or go back to where you have been. In your relationship with yourself, it is the point at which you are no longer consumed with yourself. The point at which you can be present for others."

I was only half listening as she went on.

"You will know when this happens because the quality of your relationships will change. You will be more available for others, and less concerned about getting your needs met. You will be less defensive, more open, more intimate. Think of intimacy this way: 'in to me see.'" She spelled it out like four separate words.

I nodded.

"You will be more authentic about who you are, and more willing to share who you are with the world. After you reach that crux, you will be available to deepen your relationships with others and with the Earth. Now is an opportunity to take a small step in deepening your relationship with the Earth."

"By doing what?" I was becoming very frustrated and edgy.

"Not by doing anything. You have three choices right now. You can remain here until first light, and then get back to camp, or you can be in relationship with the Earth and trust that you will make it back safely without any artificial lights. What's your choice?" She stood.

"You said three. What's the third choice?" I asked.

"Fear. You can go back to camp, but with fear as your constant companion, your body tense, and with no connection to the Earth." She started walking away, fading.

"Wait, I want to go back to camp, and I don't want to be riddled with fear. So what giant leap do I have to make now to accomplish that?" I started to go after her.

She was almost gone. All that remained was a glow and her voice. "So long as you perceive it as a giant leap, you will not succeed. You must build a bridge connecting you with the Earth, as you saw Greg doing today with the river. Feel connected, a part of the Earth, not separate from Her. Learn to trust your own instincts. Allow the bottom of your feet, and by extension your entire body and mind, to communicate with the Earth with each step. Your instincts will take you where you need to go. Trust them, trust yourself, trust the Earth. Good luck."

I was alone. I hate it when she lays a big one on me like that and then just disappears.

Chapter Eight

Tyrants

I awoke just after first light to the smell of coffee. Even though I don't drink the brew, I love its aroma. Lying there with my eyes closed, I remembered my time with Spirit Dancer the night before, but couldn't tell whether it was real or a dream. If it was real, how did I get back to camp? I couldn't remember a thing.

Cautiously I moved my legs and arms to see if there were any sore muscles or injuries that might speak of a harrowing return in the moonless night. Emerging from my sleeping bag, I checked my shins and arms for bruises, abrasions, or embedded cactus needles that would signal any falls. Nothing. My body was pain free. I concluded it must have been a dream. It would be impossible to make my way back in the dark without some mishaps, wouldn't it?

After breakfast, we loaded up and headed downstream, stopping midmorning at Saddle Canyon at mile 48. At first I didn't think we were stopping because every boat ahead floated past where I thought was the obvious stopping place.

"Aren't we stopping?" I asked Wally, my guide for the day.

Wally nodded affirmatively, "Watch," he replied, and I began to watch each boat ahead pull over into a large eddy, and then the guide stopped rowing. I soon saw that the current in an eddy circulates upstream. Without any effort on the part of the guides, each boat drifted effortlessly up to the beach.

We took our turn floating in. "Look at the current along the shore. See how strong it is. If we were to pull out of the current where you thought we should, I would be rowing directly against that current and working way too hard. So it's easier to float a hundred yards past the logical turn-in point, and let the eddy do the work."

I nodded, amazed, and he smiled at my recognition and continued. "You learn quickly to use the current to minimize the work. Maximum efficiency with minimum effort is the only way to go down here. Going with the flow may be a cliché off the river, but on the river it is our mantra. Two-hundred twenty-six miles is a long way to row in anybody's book. Our days would be a lot longer if we didn't use the river to our advantage."

That's a great metaphor for life, I thought. Let the river do the work, then all you have to do is keep your craft in the current taking you where you want to go.

After tying up, the guides assembled everyone in a shaded area with a beautiful view of the river corridor looking downstream. The Canyon continued to amaze me, and I stood there enjoying the view. Around every bend was an unparalleled mural that would make any photographer or sketch artist envious.

My thoughts were interrupted by a loud voice and I turned around to look. "Where are we going? What are we going to see?"

The question came from my least favorite passenger, Frank. He had annoyed me the first day, with his brash self-centered attitude. He was one of those larger-than-life people who always seemed to push my buttons. He was short and very broad in the shoulders, and again today, he wasn't wearing a shirt. He seemed to enjoy displaying his ample body by wearing only shorts. It was not a pretty sight. I leaned over and joked to Wally that he suffered from Dunlop's disease—his belly done lopped over his belt. He also had a very big voice, was very intelligent, and had no boundaries. Big body, big voice, big head, right in your face. As he pushed his way into the group, I discreetly moved to the other side, and turned my attention to Greg who was talking and pointing.

"We're heading for that slope in the distance, if you want to go on this hike," said Greg in his low-key cowboy drawl. As he removed the ten-gallon hat that was his trademark, I could imagine him taking charge of a Utah oil rig. I had to smile though. Somehow the hat seemed out of place with the ragged tennis shoes on his feet. He turned back to the group. "The first part of the hike will get your heart pumping, so pace yourselves and take plenty of water. We'll be in the sun until we get into the canyon. The last couple hundred yards will be wet, so wear shoes that won't get ruined if they get wet." He glanced down at his own feet and then back up, replacing his hat and looking around to see if there were questions.

"What's at the end of the hike," boomed Frank's voice again. Nothing wrong with the question, but as I looked around at some of the other passengers, I could tell they felt the same way I did about Frank.

"The canyon walls out about one-half mile up, and there's a pool fed by a low volume waterfall," responded Greg. Frank nodded, unimpressed.

I had learned in life that some people are very "destination oriented". They seem to put blinders on, and rush to the goal, missing the beauty along the way. To my surprise, Frank was not one of them.

As we began walking, I fell into step beside Wally . On every hike, it was one of the guide's jobs to bring up the rear. Wally was accepting the task today. I started a conversation and asked him what winters were like in Flagstaff, knowing he attended school there. He had barely started to reply when our attention was drawn to Frank up ahead, checking out the trees. In his loud voice he said, to no one in particular, "Look at these leaves. They're curled. It means they're diseased and in a weakened state. If they don't get water and nutrients, they will die."

I looked over at Wally noticing his interest had turned to Frank. As we walked ahead to where Frank was standing, Wally informed me, "Frank's actually a biologist. Guess he has a passing interest in botany too." No one else was paying much attention, but I was grudgingly impressed with Frank's observation. At least he was looking around and noticing more than the path and the destination.

Wally took a closer look at the trees and asked, "What do you think is wrong?" Frank replied matter-of-factly using a lot of big words and a very technical-sounding diagnosis. Then he abruptly walked away leaving Wally looking up. Wally shrugged his shoulders and we fell into step again together.

The first part of the hike was very strenuous, as Greg said it would be. The trail was cut into a steep slope that seemed to go on forever. Most of it was in the sun and I noticed Frank up ahead sweating profusely. He stopped often to catch his breath, wipe his forehead with a red bandanna, and drink water from a canteen. As out of shape as he appeared, he had amazing stamina and determination.

We finally reached the highest point on the trail, and began our descent into the side canyon. From our lofty vantage point, we could see the beginning of a very lush area where dry grasses mixed with a variety of trees. Wally pointed out catclaw acacia and redbud trees. There were ample quantities of bushes he called barberry and brickalia. As we entered the canyon, a small creek watered the banks, and to my surprise I spotted some very large thistle. I'd seen them in abundance back in the Midwest, but was surprised to find them here, in the desert.

Out of the corner of my eye, I noticed Frank looking into a pool of water.

"What do you see, Frank?" I inquired. Jane was asking a question and Wally walked on ahead to talk to her.

"Dobson fly larvae on the bottom," he replied, pointing at a small pool. "I didn't realize they were here."

He walked a little further, bent over and scooped up a translucent shell.

"Interesting. Here is the discarded shell of a Dobson fly larva." He held it up for me to see. He continued walking, looking all around. He then stopped and pointed to a dark spot on the canyon wall just above his head. "Look. There is the mature adult Dobson fly. Amazing. How often do you get to see a complete life cycle in such a small area?"

I had to admit this was impressive. Not so much the Dobson fly, although it was interesting. What amazed me the most was seeing a different side of Frank. While all the others were hurrying to the waterfall, Frank was noticing the richness of the place. At least he had one redeeming quality.

Upon reaching the waterfall, many of the passengers were already preparing to head back to the boats. Fine by me. I could enjoy its beauty without the noise of others distracting me. I walked into the pool, which was deeper than I'd expected, forcing me to swim the last fifteen feet. Holding one foot against each side of the narrow walls, I rinsed my hair in the falls. Although soap is not allowed, to protect life in the pool and creek, I came away from my shower feeling very refreshed.

On the way back to the boats, I noticed Frank sitting by a stagnant pool of water. Obviously thinking I was a kindred spirit because I'd talked to him earlier, he motioned me to join him. I hesitated at first, but figured I might learn something, since he clearly knew more about flora and fauna than I.

As I approached him, he asked me what I saw.

"Looks like scum on top of dead water to me," I said, being rather flip.

He looked somewhat surprised at my comment, but didn't miss a beat. "Do you know in this supposedly dead body of water, there are five layers of life? One on the surface, two intermediate layers in the water, one on the soil, and one in the soil. Tell you what, why don't you take my spot, and check it out?"

I agreed, and he left to continue his exploration. At first I didn't see much. But after sitting for a minute or so, I began to notice more and more movement. Various sizes and shapes of water beetles. Waterstriders floating on the surface, their feet suspended on tiny beads of air. Their shadow on the bottom appeared comically large, like the characters in an early Mickey Mouse cartoon. Dobsonfly, Damselfly, and Dragonfly larvae patrolling the bottom. The more I looked the more I saw. It was astonishing how much life there was in this tiny, stagnant pool. My stomach growled, reminding me it was almost lunch time, so I resumed my descent into camp.

When I arrived back at the boats, lunch was already being consumed. I plunged into the river to cool off and then joined the others in devouring another tasty meal. After lunch, I found a shady spot and took a much appreciated nap. I was awakened by Greg announcing our departure. We continued our journey deeper into Marble Canyon.

As the Canyon deepens, it also widens. Every so often we would get a glimpse of the North Rim floating majestically in the distance. Normally we could only see one or two layers of the sedimentary walls because of the steepness. As impressive as the walls are, seeing the rim off in the distance gives you an expanding sense of the enormity of the Canyon. It is so compelling that it becomes almost impossible to consider life beyond the 'big ditch.' Day three and I was so absorbed I felt like I'd been gone for a month. Not because it felt like I'd been here for a long time, but because I felt so far removed from that other reality. No place had ever had this kind of affect on me. Others I asked felt the same way.

We arrived at mile 53, our camp for the day, by mid-afternoon. It was called Nankoweap. I learned there are differing opinions as to the derivation of the name, but there was no confusion about its impressive nature.

Greg tried to shed some light on the name. "The Southern Paiutes called this area Ninkuipi, meaning 'Indians killed.' It seems Apache marauders forded the Colorado River and invaded a Kaibab Camp one night. They killed each sleeping Indian, except for one woman who escaped to Moccasin and related the story. Another story says the area got its name from the Paiute word meaning 'singing' or 'echo canyon'."

Directly across from camp was a huge sheer wall painted red by the iron oxide pigment from the Hermit Shale above. The late day sun created a dazzling display of brilliant color. Its reflection on the river gave the impression of a red-orange ribbon of silk snaking downstream for miles.

Above the camp was our first sign of ancient human habitation. Marian gathered us together and began a narration. She pointed to several shadowed indentations where the talus slope contacted the Canyon wall. In the one farthest upstream, I could make out four or five blackened sections looking very much like windows with dark shades drawn.

I listened intently as Marian talked. "What you are seeing are storage areas, granaries, built and used sometime between 800 and 1250 AD by the ancestors of today's Hopi, Zuni and Pueblo Peoples, commonly known as the Anasazi. Actually, Anasazi is a Navajo word that is considered derogatory to the Hopi. It means 'ancient enemy.' The Hopi prefer the name Hisatsinom, which means 'those who came before.' But because the Zuni and Pueblo also claim an historical connection, a compromise was struck, and some guides now refer to the Anasazi as the Pueblo People."

I was intrigued by the location of these granaries. Was it possible to carry heavy loads of grain up to those storage areas? While everyone else began the setup for the evening, I decided to get a better feel for them. If I hurried, I might be able to capture the sunset from up there with my camera.

I followed a trail which appeared to have been beaten down over the years by the native inhabitants and wildlife. Human footsteps from the commercial rafting expeditions formed an even more pronounced trail. At the beginning I was surrounded by large, bush-like mesquite and acacia trees. Then I started up a trail that led to the top of the delta where the hike to the granaries would begin in steep, aerobic earnest. I was learning that life is truly a perceptual experience. As I hiked, I tried to place myself in the shoes (or sandals and bare feet) of those who had lived there a thousand years before. I tried to imagine carrying fifty to a hundred pounds of grain up the incredibly steep trail. I could not. Yet it was a fact. They had done it. It was, indeed, normal to them. To me it was an aerobic nightmare.

I reached the granaries after the sun had dropped below the canyon rim, but in time to see a spectacular view of the river corridor looking downstream. The long silvery snake ended abruptly about four miles downstream where the walls turned sharply to the left. The rock strata near the top was bathed in gold. I began framing the scene by adjusting my camera's zoom lens. First a vertical close up, then a horizontal. Then I moved the lens inward for a wider angle. I snapped like crazy hoping to capture the mood.

"Not a bad view, eh, Charly. Was it worth the effort?" I recognized Spirit Dancer's voice, but couldn't see her. The voice seemed to be coming from inside the granaries. As I searched, she appeared, walking right though one of the walls of the ancient structure.

"Why am I surprised that you should be here?" I replied. "And the answer is yes, it's a spectacular view. It takes my breath away."

"A thousand years ago it was not selected for the view." She moved her arm in a gentle sweeping motion toward the opposite end of the structures. I could almost feel the velvet-like surface of her white deerskin wrap. I was tempted to reach out and touch it.

She continued, "Those who farmed this delta could never take their food for granted. They might have a drought year and produce very little. Or there might be unusually large flash floods that could wipe out their crops. The river was much different then, as you have heard. They chose this location to ensure the safety of the crops they did produce. After harvest a portion was brought up here to store over the winter, so when they returned in the spring, they would have food and seed stock for the spring planting. The rest they consumed or took with them when they migrated to the North Rim in the fall. This location assured relative safety from animal and human predators, and it was also protected from the weather."

"Thanks for the anthropology lesson. But I'm sure you have other reasons for paying me this visit," I said.

She moved to sit in one of the darkened holes that I guessed might have once been a window or door. "You are correct. Today you received some very important information about who you are. What did you observe?"

I lowered myself to sit cross-legged before her and looked up. I was getting into this and proud that I had observed several things I felt were important. "I watched the guides use the current to move the boats with relative ease. And I also learned some things from Frank, who I don't much like. Apparently no one else does either."

"How did the guides use the current, Charly. How would you describe what they did?" She adjusted the robe and then gave me her full attention.

"They watched how the current moved, and knew that by floating a hundred yards past our landing spot they could use the current to take them back to where they wanted to go without even pulling on the oars. If they pulled out where I thought they should, they would have worked a lot harder. Instead, there was almost no effort. It may not be a big deal just once or twice, but this trip is 226 miles long. Over that length, working harder would take a lot more out of them. Wally described it as 'maximum efficiency with minimum effort.'"

"I refer to it as 'effort-less energy,'" she interjected. "Expending as little effort as possible to accomplish your objectives. You might call it more bang for your buck." She smiled, enjoying her own humor. I smiled back and she continued.

"This is more obvious at the physical level, because you can see what needs to be done and determine how best to do it without getting burned out. It is more difficult on the mental and emotional planes, and that is what I want to talk about here. But before I do, let's take a quick look at your experience with Frank today. What did you notice?" Her head cocked slightly as she waited for my answer.

I didn't have to think on this one. "I noticed how impatient everyone is with him because he's constantly asking questions, and he doesn't care whether he interrupts others. He's loud, gets right in your face, and he's gross. During the hike, however, I actually developed some respect for him."

"Interesting. How did that happen?" she asked.

"Well, everyone else just rushed off and headed for the waterfall. I noticed Frank walking by himself looking around. He was inspecting a grove of trees that appeared to be in a weakened state. A little while later he pointed out some bug larva, the discarded shell of the larva and even an adult insect. He took time to show me the whole life cycle. It was interesting. And, on the way down I found him staring into a stagnant pool of water. It looked lifeless until he pointed out all the different ecosystems. Then I looked at it in a different way. I was very impressed with his knowledge and attitude."

Gazing off down the River corridor she said, "And, what did you learn from all that?"

"Well, I saw how much the others missed by rushing off. People miss a lot when they are in a hurry to get somewhere. I also learned about the living Earth and how important it is to not judge something, or someone for that matter, by its cover. Like the stagnant pool. We do that all the time with people who are different. And, take this desert. At first glance it looks almost dead, but it is starting to grow on me, and part of that is because of Frank. I know there is so much more for us to experience if we just slow down, especially if we're willing to look beneath the surface."

"That's all very valuable insight, Charly," Spirit Dancer remarked. "It's also very mental. What did the hike teach you about Frank, and more importantly, about you?"

"I don't follow," I replied, wondering where she was going with this one.

Her dark eyes were back on me and I felt a little uneasy. "You have some judgments about Frank. Are they helpful in getting to know him?"

"Those aren't judgments, they're facts. Everybody thinks he's a jerk, and they don't want to have anything to do with him." I said defensively.

She raised her eyebrows and cocked her head again. "I can see that. So, Frank has nothing to offer anybody here, is that what you're saying?"

"No, I'm saying nobody likes the guy. He's loud, he gets in your..."

She held up her hand and interrupted me. "Its not necessary to repeat yourself. Walk around the Wheel a little. You don't like Frank, and no one else appears to either. Yet he may have given you one of the greatest gifts you'll receive during this trip. Often people who behave like Frank are covering up their own insecurities. No one says you have to become bosom buddies, but obviously he has something to offer. So what's the lesson?"

It was my turn and I reflected for a minute. "I guess it's the lesson I learned from the stagnant pool. On the surface it is ugly and looks like it has nothing to offer me. In fact I wouldn't even be curious about a place like that. Frank helped me see richness I would have missed."

She was nodding and the copper feathers on her necklace tinkled. "So, Frank is like that pool. On the surface he repulses people and they never get the chance to discover the richness within him." She paused a second and sat up straighter. "Excellent. Everybody has something to offer. Sometimes you have to dig a little deeper. Along the same lines, everyone is brilliant, when it's safe for them to be who they are. People like Frank don't feel safe being themselves, so they put on a thick suit of armor and push their way through life. You could learn a lot about yourself from Frank, do you realize that?"

I was getting stiff sitting, so I stood and stretched a little. "Apparently not. How?"

"Remember yesterday I told you not to take your tyrants too seriously?" She stood too, and we both looked down at the River.

"Yes, and I asked you what a tyrant was. Guess I'm about to find out."

"Everyone has them. Everybody is one. Tyrants are people, situations and circumstances that push your buttons. Frank seems to be pushing everyone's buttons, so he qualifies. One Native American teaching says, 'Bless your tyrants because they are here to accelerate your learning.' If you want to learn, stalk the tyrant, meaning observe the tyrant, and discover what it is it has to teach. You just learned some of what Frank is teaching you. Now I want you to take the next step. When you integrate this one, you will definitely accelerate your road to freedom."

This was as close as we'd been. We were only about three feet apart. How she had walked through that wall a few moments ago amazed me. She looked very solid, like a regular human being. I wanted to reach out and touch her, but felt it might be inappropriate.

I wondered if she was reading my mind. She smiled and went on. "My point is all that mental information is helpful, and what you learned from Frank today will serve you for the rest of your life. But, like most other humans who are still asleep, you are missing a key element in personal growth."

"What would that be?" I needed to move and paced a few steps.

"You are keeping what you see in the actions of other people, in situations and in circumstances, 'out there.' You are not bringing it back to yourself. If you see beauty in the world, it is within you.

Bring it back and honor it as part of who you are. If you see the beast out there, it is also within you. Bring it back, acknowledge it as an aspect of you, and make peace with it. So, when you are faced with either situation, beauty or beast, ask yourself this question, 'What is this person, situation, or circumstance teaching me about me?' Do you follow?"

"I do." A light bulb had gone on. She had my undivided attention again.

"Well then, let's practice. What did your experience with Frank today teach you about you?" she asked.

I groaned, but then thought about her question for several minutes. "I don't know if this is in the ballpark, or should I say canyon, but it's the best I can do right now." I turned and she was watching me. "Frank is very outspoken. He doesn't hesitate to state his opinion. And he doesn't seem to care what others think about him. If I bring that back to me, it means I'm very outspoken. I'm opinionated, and I don't care what others think of me. Is that correct?"

"What do you think?" Spirit Dancer was not about to rescue me on this one.

"I've never considered myself outspoken or opinionated. And, I think I've been far too concerned about what others think of me. It's just the opposite. I don't understand." I was puzzled.

"Go a little deeper, Charly. You're right on the edge of a big discovery." She turned away, put her toes on the edge and looked down at the river again.

"This is bizarre. I need help." This was too deep for me.

"Do you like how much energy you put in to what others think of you?" she asked.

That was an easy one. "No, I hate it."

"Is it possible you have some respect for Frank buried under your judgment, simply because he doesn't waste a lot of time worrying about what others think?"

I hated to admit it. "It is possible. No, I do respect that, and hate it too. Oh, no. I get it. I judge Frank because he is outspoken, and he doesn't seem to care. Does that mean I want to be like him?"

Spirit Dancer nodded slightly, "Not exactly. Frank has no boundaries, he hasn't learned—when he's violating people's space. He's unaware that he is offensive to others. You're beginning to understand that. And yes, you envy his ability to be outspoken, and you would like to put a limit on how much you care about other people's opinions of you."

"So in Frank, I'm seeing a very underdeveloped side of me that I would like to develop. True?" I asked.

Her head bobbed up and down, and she went on, "Yes, and it's accurate to use the term underdeveloped. Because in truth you are outspoken, you are opinionated, and there is a part of you that can be so in spite of the opinions of others. So you don't have to go out and look for it, you just have to allow it to emerge. You may take some bumps and bruises along the way until you become competent at stating your opinions so that others will be receptive to them." She paused, then continued, "One of the most important questions you must have in your arsenal is, 'What is this tyrant teaching me about me?'"

I nodded, trying to picture myself as outspoken as she indicated I already was.

She brought me back to reality, and I realized she had walked into the granary and was looking through one of the black holes. "Now, there is more to this teaching. It is a very rich one. But we will save it for another time, along with more on Effortless Energy at the mental level. It's getting darker. Better get started back to camp, or you'll have a repetition of last night. Pleasant dreams, Charly. This was an important day for you."

She was leaving. "Wait!" I shouted. "Does that mean last night wasn't a dream?" I climbed to the hole and looked inside, being careful not to touch the fragile walls. In the darkness all I could see was the white robe swaying and it was dimming fast. She was gone. I didn't have any time to think about last night. She was right, it was getting dark. So I took off down the trail.

When I arrived at camp, I felt exhilarated. The run down required intense concentration, and it felt great to push my edge. The others had finished eating, and at first I thought I'd missed out. Then I saw Dean.

"Where have you been? Saved you a plate, but it's probably cold." He said.

Cold or not I slammed it down, and went immediately to set up my camp. I lay down with a deep sigh, feeling the relief of getting off my feet. I shut my eyes for a few minutes, and when I opened them it was fully dark. Looking up at the star filled ceiling above me, another shooting star slashed across the canyon. I got up on my elbows and tried to see the other camps. Either everyone was asleep, or I was the only one to see it, because there were no exclamations from anywhere.

I was intrigued, and would check around in the morning to see if anyone had seen either this one or the previous one. Within seconds I was sound asleep.

In my dreams I heard thunder. But it wasn't a dream. Raindrops jolted me out of my deep sleep. I looked around as others began scurrying to set up their tents. What had they said at orientation? I hoped I could remember. Bursts of lightning illuminated the wall across the river. By the time I found my flashlight, I was fully awake. The storm was right overhead. The thunder and lightening were almost simultaneous. The ground shook with each clash of the cymbals.

The camp was in chaos. Passengers who had never set up a tent in their lives were panicking. I at least had the advantage of seeing Dean do it before. It was complicated enough in the light. At night, with only head lamps and the occasional lightning flash for light, it was well nigh impossible.

Suddenly I heard a strange noise. It sounded like the howl of a coyote. Why would a coyote start howling in the middle of a storm? Then I realized it wasn't a coyote at all. With each lightening flash the guides were howling like coyotes celebrating a kill. The immediate thunder seemed to feed their exhilaration. They were actually enjoying themselves, and the feeling became contagious. They seemed to thrive on these sudden storms. The mood in camp turned from panic to fun.

When a strong wind combined with the driving rain, I ran to hold down my tent. Dean yelled that if I wasn't careful I was going to have a hang glider. Everyone laughed. The ground underneath me still shook with each blast of thunder, and my tent lit up in unison with each discharge of lightning, but everyone was taking it in stride. A few people were even dancing in the rain.

All the tents were finally erected, and I heard Marian shout, "I don't know about you idiots, but I'm getting wet." She dove into her tent. A number of others followed, me included.

The storm went on for a couple of hours, and just as suddenly as it arrived, it departed. All that remained were the distant rumblings of the thunder gods as the system journeyed up the Canyon to rattle other visitors.

Chapter Nine

Passion,
Purpose,
and
Priorities

I had forgotten I was supposed to be on the breakfast cook crew, and was awakened out of a deep sleep by Greg. It took me a few minutes to regain consciousness, and then I stumbled to the kitchen. On the way, I noticed the river had changed color again, from an emerald clear green to the Colorado red we had seen temporarily after the thunderstorm on the second day.

Greg had heated the water and was just adding the coffee grounds as I arrived on the scene. He told me to make the juice and start toasting the muffins on the griddle.

Five minutes later I saw him lift the conch shell to his lips. The sound was soft and resonant, unlike most bedroom alarm clocks that get people started on the wrong foot. There was an immediate line of sleepy faces, as many had already been awakened by the aroma of the brewing coffee.

"What's for breakfast," came Frank's booming voice. "I'm so hungry I could eat a horse."

"You already have," replied Greg, a smile showing in the slight upturn at the corner of his mouth. "Eggs to order, muffins, sausages, cereal, and grape juice. We'll be blowing the conch for the eggs as soon as the muffins are ready. Give us about ten minutes. If you're looking for something to do, the water needs pumping."

"No thanks," Frank replied. "I'm on vacation. I didn't pay all this money to bust my butt doing your job." He grabbed his coffee and went down to the river.

"Do you have jerks like that on every trip?" I asked Greg when Frank was out of earshot.

"Not very often. You just learn to give people like Frank a lot of space. He's not a bad guy. He was on my boat yesterday, and he is very intelligent. Does some very interesting work with the National Institute of Health. Way too sophisticated to even explain. Sure can be annoying though, can't he?" Greg started preparing the sausages in a Dutch Oven.

"I don't much care for him, but I learned a hell of a lot from him during that hike up Saddle yesterday. He really helped me see this place in a new way. And, I have some respect for that. If he wasn't such a jerk." I shook my head.

"I learned a long time ago that the people who bug me can be a real gift," Greg said softly. "I don't pay much attention to their behavior unless it puts people at risk, or someone complains."

I looked up, surprised to hear Greg's use of the word gift. That was the same word Spirit Dancer had used. I thought for a second and then commented, "I know what you mean about people being a gift. It's a new way for me to look at anyone who pushes my buttons, and I'm working on that with Frank. I guess you can learn a lot about people in this job."

He was getting additional items from the cooler. "If you pay attention. Actually most of our passengers are good folks who get a lot out of being here. My job is to make sure they get a chance to experience as much of the Canyon as possible. When they go back home, many of them will have at least a new appreciation for the environment and issues like water politics. People from the north and east have very little awareness of the water problems we face in this country. You're from Michigan, right?"

"Yep." I said.

"With the Great Lakes surrounding you, I doubt you're too concerned about conserving water, am I right?" He headed back to the stoves looking over his shoulder at me.

"You're right. I've heard a friend in Denver talk about it though. They have to ration water and can only water their grass on certain days. I'm still pretty ignorant. But I'd like to know more. What's the most important thing for me to know?" I watched Greg pick up the conch shell and get ready to announce breakfast.

He paused a minute before blowing. "I've got some books I can lend you. *A River No More*, by Philip Fradkin, *Cadillac Desert*, by Marc Reisner, and *A Story That Stands Like a Dam*, by Russell Martin. They'll give you a good understanding of the history of water issues in the west, as well as good insight into the Colorado River and Glen Canyon dam. After you've thumbed through them, we can have a talk."

"Okay," I replied, a little disappointed at not getting the scoop right then. But, the sausages were golden brown, the eggs were ready to be cooked, and Greg was giving the conch shell a long blast. I then watched him demonstrate the skills of a short order cook as he dished out orders from scrambled, to over-easy, to dead-and-buried.

As usual, all the guides were busy. As I watched Greg handle the kitchen, I noticed Marian pumping water through the filter, the job Frank had turned down. Wally carried black bags containing passengers' sleeping bags and clothing to James's boat. Meanwhile Dean ran around and topped off the air in each boat.

It had become clear there was something to do from dawn to dusk, which made the guide's cheery, enthusiastic attitude all the more amazing. I could never work this hard and maintain such a positive feeling. I was becoming wistful about finding work that I could feel this good about. In truth, until this trip, I just assumed that only a fortunate few could ever find jobs they loved this much. I wanted to feel like they did. And there was no way that was going to happen, at least not in my current job.

During breakfast, I asked several people if they had seen the shooting star last night. No one had. I guess they were all asleep. Still, I was starting to wonder if there was some connection to Spirit Dancer. I would have to ask her next time she showed up.

After breakfast, Marian talked about what we could expect on the river. It would be a pretty mellow day, with one good-sized rapid three miles downstream, and a few smaller ones. The focus for this day was the Little Colorado River, about eight miles away. "When it is clear," Marian stated, "it is a rich turquoise blue, and best of all it is so warm you'll have to go swimming. When we reach there, if it is clear, we will be staying for several hours. If it's muddy, there will be a Plan B."

No one had any questions for Marian, so Greg announced a hike up to the granaries, where I had visited the night before. "It's a short but steep hike that will be a little challenging for some of you. But it is one of the most spectacular views in the Canyon, and it will be worth your climb. Also, it will be good training for those of you who are hiking out at Phantom Ranch."

The latter was a reference to Richard and the forty-something women and their daughters who had only signed up for the first six days. They would have to hike out the Bright Angel Trail, which is seven and one-half miles long and covers an elevation change of 4600 feet. The top of the trail ends at the Grand Canyon Village and Visitor's Center on the South Rim, where they would be transported to Flagstaff. Richard was in his forties, and I'd noticed the first day that he was about fifty pounds overweight. This hike would be a good test of his stamina. But, whether he fared well on this one or not, he was still going to have to hike out Bright Angel. The old saying came to mind, "If I'd known I was going to live this long, I would have taken better care of my body." It fit Richard.

We set off with Dean leading. He's not very tall, maybe 5'10", but he walks like he has the legs of someone 6'3". He sets a very fast pace, but I was used to it from the hiking we'd done in Michigan. Within the first couple hundred yards the group was dividing into those who wanted to keep up with Dean, and those who didn't. I decided to stay up front. As most of his previous sixth-grade students would attest, he had volumes of information stored away, and if you weren't within ear shot, you would miss a lot.

Dean stopped to let the stragglers catch up. We were entering the very steep part of the trail. He began a discussion of how the delta had been formed from sediment building up from debris flowing out of the side canyon during flash floods. Suddenly we heard a loud crack!

We all spun around, but Richard was the first to see what was happening. "Look!!" he yelled, pointing to the sheer cliff across the river.

"Rock fall!!" Wally shouted.

A huge slab from the Supai formation, about 1,200 feet above the river, was breaking apart as it slammed against the rock wall below it. At first there was a series of loud reports as the rock broke into smaller pieces. Then there was an eerie silence as the rain of debris began its thousand foot free fall. Staccato thuds were heard as tons of large and small rocks announced their earthly arrival, and a small cloud of dust began rising.

Wally and Marian had dropped their packs and were running wildly towards the end of the delta to get a better look. The rock fall was restricted to the other side of the river and was not posing a danger to any of us. A huge billowing cloud was filling the entire stretch of river, and was slowly drifting downstream.

What a sight! A hundred foot slab of rock 300 million years old, had finally succumbed to gravitational pull and was beginning its journey to the sea, where it would take on another rock form millions of years from now.

When the initial excitement wore off, Dean called everyone together. "This is a graphic example of what we call weathering, one of the most dominant forms of erosion in the Canyon. Evidently the thunderstorm from last night was the last straw in the evolutionary dance of the rock. Earth activity had created cracks, which represented the first stage of erosion. Over the eons, untold numbers of storms brought rain into the cracks. In the winter the moisture froze and expanded, loosening the rock, increasing the cracks again. Vibrations from millions of thunder claps added more instability. One last storm proved to be pivotal. And you got to see it."

"Amazing!" was all Richard could say as he shook his head looking over at the receding cloud.

Jane actually looked a little pale, and didn't say much.

Frank began an intense technical discussion directed to whomever would listen.

I waited for Wally and Marian to return, and we continued the hike. Everyone was thrilled and the chatter continued all the way to the granaries. Again, those with more stamina surged ahead with

Dean, and the rest trailed out behind talking in groups. Wally , Marian, and I passed the slower moving passengers about half way up.

We joined the first group arriving well ahead of the rest. As we looked down, the trail appeared even steeper. The stragglers were strung out like a very long snake. At the end was Richard, who seemed to rest after each step. Finally, everyone was assembled within earshot of Dean who began a discussion on the history of the granaries. He also provided information about the geology of the area, and some of the controversies still surrounding them. It seems that no one was around 240 to 400 million years ago when the rock layers were forming, so geology is still an inexact science.

He told us that one of the other areas of interest at Nankoweap is the creek that is a spawning ground for rainbow trout. As an introduced species they have only been present in the Canyon for less than two decades. Recently there has been an influx of bald eagles stopping for a tasty meal during their migration. One interesting story Dean shared was how the ravens, who are carrion feeders, learned to fish by observing the eagle.

Ravens are very smart birds, and are considered by some indigenous tribes to be the bringer of magic. Feathers from the bird are always present during healing ceremonies as a reflection of raven's healing power. But, to many people they are just noisy scavengers. As we had learned, in the Canyon the raven is the first visitor after boats depart from camp each day. No matter how careful we were the ravens managed to vacuum up any microscopic particles of food left by an inattentive diner. Sometimes they even squawked at us as we headed downstream, as if to say, "Couldn't you have been a little more generous?"

It was time to head for the Little Colorado playground, so we returned to camp and again played musical boats selecting our raft and guide for the day. I decided to go with Marian along with Jane and Richard. I hadn't spoken much with Jane since our experience together on the first day, so it would be good to catch up with her. One thing was certain, she was not the same woman who'd stood at Lees Ferry fearing the unknown. She was alive, her eyes sparkled, and she was no longer hunkered down in the back of the raft. Just as she predicted, she could be seen each day in the front, going through the rapids, her laugh a testament to her new found spirit.

Richard was still recovering from the hike to the ruins. He appeared exhausted, and headed to the back of the raft finding a comfortable spot to relax.

During the hike, a strong wind had come up. We only had eight miles to the Little "C", and there was only one good sized rapid in the stretch. Kwagunt was three miles downstream. Marian said it normally took less than an hour to get there, but today it took almost twice that long, cutting into our play time. I was amazed at how determined Marian was rowing against the upstream wind. She was about 5'9", but didn't appear particularly strong. Even so, she kept up the same pace as all the bigger, stronger males. She also provided a constant stream of information about the Canyon, including the geology and, especially, the human history. She informed us that we would be passing the largest known habitation site tomorrow. She appeared genuinely excited about going there.

During one of her pauses, I asked, "How many trips have you done down here, Marian?"

"Around sixty to seventy, I'd say. I don't keep track anymore," she replied between strokes.

"What were you doing before you became a guide?" It was a question I was to later find out was as common as, "How deep is the river?," and "What do you do in the off season?""

Smiling, she said, "I was an executive secretary in Los Angeles, working for one of the studios."

"Wow! What a change," I responded, honestly impressed. "How did you become interested in river rafting?"

"In the early seventies a good friend talked me into going on a raft trip in the Canyon. I wasn't too thrilled with the idea, but I wanted to spend some time with him, so I agreed. Before the trip was half over, I was hooked." She looked over to see my reaction. I nodded, wanting her to go on. "A year later I quit my job, enrolled in whitewater school in northern California, caught on with a river company in the northwest, and eventually made it down here."

"That's great. You quit a high paying job with a movie studio in LA, and without any experience decided you were going to become a river guide?" My voice reflected definite amazement.

She nodded affirmatively with a "it wasn't a big deal look" on her face, then said, "I didn't have much to lose. If it didn't work out, I could've always gone back to what I was doing."

"Well that may be true," I interjected, "but how many people do you know who are willing to just chuck it all and go do something so totally different?"

"More than you know, obviously," Marian replied. "Talk to anybody on this crew and you'll hear a similar story. As you know, Dean was a teacher, Greg a welder. Ahhh, James still is a financial consultant who takes most of the summer off, and Wally is a student working towards a biology degree, and hoping to someday land a job in a National Park. To be honest with you, if I had known what I would have to go through to get here, I probably wouldn't have done it. But I was lucky. I had some very good teachers, and I managed to pick things up fast enough that I didn't embarrass anyone, except myself a few times." She chuckled with the last comment and winked. I was wondering if she knew about my rowing experience.

I knew she wasn't telling the whole story. Dean had told me there weren't all that many women rowing boats professionally when Marian started out. She had been one of the first dozen or so women to work in the Grand Canyon. Dean had commented that she must have put up with a lot of "macho crap" along the way, from a "good old boys" group that wasn't all that excited about having women on their crews. Still, there was no doubt that now she was a valued and valuable member of this crew, which worked together better than any team I'd ever seen. She carried her own weight and more, and was as good a guide as any of the men. I had just heard at breakfast that she was the only member of the crew that had never flipped her boat.

Thinking about my own dissatisfaction, and looking for some hope, I absent-mindedly asked, "Do you find many passengers who are influenced by stories like yours, who go back and quit their jobs?" I tilted my head forward and looked over at her.

"A few. Charly, have you been bitten?" she was laughing. I shrugged my shoulders and grinned. She became serious again. "We don't hear from most of our passengers once they leave the trip. I know many people are dissatisfied with their jobs or their lives, but they're not willing to do what it takes to make a change. I knew I wasn't happy in my job, but it took someone dragging me to this place before I realized how unhappy I was. At the time I quit, I didn't see it as taking courage." Both of us were deep in thought. Then she continued, "But as I look back on it, it's not something most people could or should do."

"What do you mean?" I asked, perplexed by her reply.

"Look, I'm a single woman, with no responsibilities other than to myself. I don't have a husband or kids, so I can make choices that don't involve others in the same way. I can be more selfish about what I do. It's more difficult if you have kids. Besides, most people romanticize this job. You have to be willing to live more on the edge to do something like this. We don't get paid well, it's seasonal, we're away from home for extended periods which makes it hell on relationships, and it's a physically demanding job. Most people aren't willing to do what this job requires." She turned to look at me with a silent question on her face, "are you"?

I saw the negatives, but it was obvious that she loved what she was doing. "But you all seem so passionate about your work. I've never seen people work so hard or so well together."

"Thank you. What you say is true. But think about it. We have to work well together. Can you imagine what it would be like to do ten or twelve trips a year with people who don't get along, or who don't pull their own weight? It's hell, I can tell you. But, we all love this place, so it's easier to deal with all the hard work and harsh conditions. I feel very fortunate to have this job and be here. Its just not for everyone." She pointed with her right hand still holding on to the oar, "Here we go."

I glanced up and came quickly back to reality. The conversation had been interrupted by Kwagunt rapid, which provided a temporary respite from the harsh upstream winds. As soon as we hit the tail waves, however, the wind took over again. Marian resumed her methodical rowing.

Speaking to everyone in the raft, she said, "We have five miles to the Little "C", so get comfortable. There's not much more to do but stay in the current. We'll get there when we get there."

There was no bitterness or frustration in her voice. Instead it simply implied this is the way it is, so let's make the best of it.

My curiosity was too much. "How do you stay so centered when you have this constant wind. Doesn't it get to you?" I asked.

She answered immediately, "If I let it get to me, I wouldn't be working down here. I would prefer we not have this kind of wind, but I'm the visitor here, not the wind. When it blows like this I just remind myself that I chose to be here. And I chose to be here with what is here, not what I would prefer. That means heavy upstream winds, or low water, or rains, or all three. Of course, it also helps that I want to be here. A lot of my passengers would prefer to be in some other job than the one they have." She looked at me in a quizzical way again.

"I know the feeling," I interjected. "So is that all there is to it? You have some condition over which you have no control, in this case heavy upstream winds, and you remind yourself you chose to be here with whatever comes up? That's how you can keep rowing and look so calm about it?"

"There's one other thing that's more important. It's more of an attitude, " she said.

"Attitude?" I asked.

"Yes. I focus on my purpose for being here. Early on I didn't have a purpose, and it was easy to let these external circumstances like weather or personalities get in the way. During one of my trips I was having a particularly difficult time with a passenger who was a lot like Frank." She paused and looked directly at me. I raised my eyebrows, and she went on. "I overheard your conversation with Wally yesterday." I nodded. "One day I couldn't take it any more and I said some things I shouldn't have. That night the trip leader and I had a talk and he asked me what my purpose was for being a river guide. I didn't have an answer, and I didn't see how it would have changed anything.

"He told me that situations like the one that day were frequent, and he had always had the same response I had. Finally, a passenger helped him see that his reaction was simply a message." She paused, resting for a couple of beats.

"What kind of message?" I asked.

She was rowing again. "It was a signal that he was off purpose. He said the tension, and more importantly, the reaction, were less likely to happen if you were on purpose. He suggested I determine my purpose for being here. And so I did. And I have rarely lost it since."

Now I was really intrigued. "Well, what is your purpose?"

"My focus is on creating the best possible river experience for my passengers. It takes the focus off me, and it makes it easier to keep on long after I would like to stop. For instance, imagine it's later in the afternoon and this wind is still howling. After awhile my body is going to get pretty tired of rowing against it and will want to stop. It would be easy to do that, except I have the stove, and eating in the light is part of having a successful experience down here. So remembering my purpose is like keeping my priorities straight. It's like a magnet that keeps drawing me downstream. If, on the other hand, I forgot that purpose and just focused on my body screaming at me, we wouldn't get to camp till after dark. Does that make sense?"

I nodded in agreement. "I never heard purpose described that way. And yes, it makes a lot of sense. I've never even thought about having a purpose for my job. I wonder if that would make a difference?"

"It should," she nodded, "or it will tell you that you're in the wrong field, if you're accurate about what it is."

I needed time to think. "That's a lot to chew on. I'll give you a break and get my salivary glands engaged so I can digest this. Thanks for the information. It's really helpful . . . I think!"

Marian smiled and kept on rowing.

What she had said made a lot of sense, but I was disturbed that after 35 years I had so little understanding of what I was all about. I certainly didn't have a clue as to my purpose in my work. I thought about the Puzzle Theory that Spirit Dancer had spoken of, and how it might fit in. Was my purpose somewhere in my box? I filed that thought away for my next conversation with her.

That decision made, I leaned back against some of the black bags and took in the sights. After Kwagunt, the Canyon started to change. We were coming to the end of Marble Canyon, and the Canyon itself was opening up more. We were in a formation called Bright Angel Shale. I remembered Dean's explanation from one of our pre-trip lectures. It's composed of horizontal lines of purples, greens, and grays and is a soft rock that erodes easily. As a result, slopes are created that move the canyon walls away from the river. This was one way the Canyon widened to as much as sixteen miles from one rim to the other. By now we were 3,500 feet into the earth, and the vistas of the North Rim off to our right were incredible.

"What were you and Marian talking about all that time, Charly?" It was Richard, who was finally looking alive again.

"Some very interesting and somewhat disturbing stuff about purpose and doing what you love to do." I replied.

"Sounds like something I should hear about. Could you share it with me some time?" he asked.

"Sure. How about at camp tonight?" I said.

He half-laughed, "That will work, unless I fall asleep. That hike was a bit much for this overweight, out of shape body."

I didn't comment on that, but said, "I know this is your first camping experience. Are you sleeping okay?"

"Like a baby. I never believed I could feel so comfortable sleeping outside. This is the best trip I've ever been on." He slid himself up onto the side of the raft. He was alive.

"Even with that hike today?" I chided.

"Oh yes," he added a little sheepishly, staring off at the opposite shoreline, "I learned something really important today."

"What was that, if I might ask," I didn't want to get too personal.

He looked straight at me. "Well, most of the way up that incredibly steep trail, I was tempted to turn around. I can't remember working so hard. I don't know why I kept going, but I'm really glad I did. Because when I got to the top and caught my breath, the view practically took it away again. I hope my pictures come out.

"Anyway, the lesson from that hike is that there are lots of times in life when I want to quit, and often I do. This time I didn't. I kept going, and the reward was spectacular. I'll never forget that view, and the next time I'm tempted to turn back, I'll remember today and keep going." He said it with real determination. I knew he would.

"The next time, like maybe day after tomorrow when you have to hike out?" I teased.

"Don't remind me. But yes, probably. Anyway, that day I won't have a choice if I want to make my plane home."

Marian interrupted and we all turned. "We're here."

"Where?" Richard asked.

"The Little Colorado," Marian replied.

"I don't see anything," Jane stated, looking for clues of a merging river.

Marian was enjoying herself. "Be patient and you'll see in a couple of minutes. Get ready for an incredible visual treat. If it's clear, that is. And I think it will be."

We all shaded our eyes with our hands and searched downstream for some indication of blue water merging with the green of the Colorado. Then we rounded a point on the left and gasped with delight.

"How beautiful," exclaimed Jane. "You're right, Marian, it is a visual delight."

"Incredible," whispered Richard. "What a contrast with the Colorado. How is it possible?"

Marian began an explanation, and I realized this was just one of the ways she achieved her purpose, helping passengers share and understand the marvels of the place she loved so much. I watched her intently and envied her passion. "It comes from a spring several miles up the drainage. The color is a combination of calcium carbonate in the water and the reflection of the blue sky. We'll be stopping here for lunch and a couple hours of play. If you need to pee, go upstream at least a hundred yards away from the Little "C".

There is a small population of an endangered fish here called the humpback chub. They're protected." As she finished, I balanced on the side of the raft and prepared to jump from the boat. "Take your life jackets with you and be careful. The mud here is very slick."

As if on cue, I stepped off the raft and slipped, plunging into the Little Colorado. Half embarrassed, I acted like the dip was planned. "Come on in you guys. The water is delightful." I didn't fool anyone.

Marian made one last comment between bursts of laughter, "Oh, and remember don't drink this water unless you want to spend a lot of time on the toilet."

Frantically, I tried to remember if my mouth had been open when I fell.

Chapter Ten

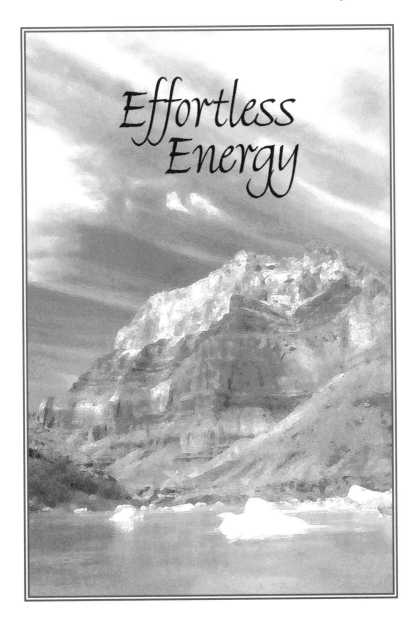

Effortless Energy

I needed time alone, so I made a couple of sandwiches, grabbed an orange and some cookies, and headed up the Little Colorado drainage. As spectacular as the Canyon had been, nothing prepared me for this. The river was a medium shade of turquoise, and there was a white residue on the bottom that reflected the robin's-egg blue sky, deepening the shade in the river to an almost surrealistic color.

It didn't take long for me to leave the others behind. I imagined myself transported back in time. First I was an early prospector looking for gold, and then a young Hopi warrior on a quest to collect salt from the sacred Hopi salt mines a couple of miles downstream. I walked past a shallow area where the water flowed over rocks formed in stair-step fashion. A short distance farther I passed a small cascade where water flowing between two rocks formed a chute. I made a mental note, "On my way back down, I think I'll try swimming through that chute."

Finally, I came to a spot that beckoned me to stay. There was a very large boulder that looked like concrete, with angular stones embedded throughout. It looked as if a stone mason had pressed them into wet cement in some random pattern of shapes, sizes and colors. The current flowed past the boulder which jutted out into the river, forming a lagoon-like pool. When I climbed up on the rock, I could tell the water was very deep. I couldn't resist the temptation, so I jumped into the soothing warm water. Rising to the surface, I floated on my back, legs and arms splayed wide in a position of ecstasy. Even though the water temperature was only 70 degrees, it felt very comfortable when compared to the 48 degree Big Colorado. I dog-paddled and treaded water for some time, just soaking in the feeling and the sights.

After enjoying a leisurely lunch, saving the cookies and half my orange for the walk back, I found a shady spot and lay down for a nap. But not for long.

"Greetings Charly. Enjoying your nap?"

It was Spirit Dancer peering down at me.

"I was," I replied caustically. "How long have I been asleep?" I didn't want to move.

"All your life, my friend. But it's good to see you waking up, slow as it is." She scrambled effortlessly up the rock I'd used to jump off. She began making herself comfortable and I knew she planned on being there for a while.

"I'll take that as a compliment." I said, sitting up.

She moved her long black hair from the front of her shoulders with both hands, brought it up and back and then let it fall behind her. A strange thought struck me. Could a spirit actually feel temperature? Was she as hot as I was? Finally she spoke. "Take it as you wish. I'm not here to give you strokes."

"Well, then what brings you here?" I asked.

"You have observed several instances of the guides working with natural rhythms, the current, the winds. And you have been impressed, not only with how they tap into those rhythms, but also with how effortless their movements often are." She studied me to see if I was agreeing with her statements.

"That's true. I've never seen anybody turn what is an obviously difficult job into a pleasurable one better than they do. I talked to Marian for quite a while about having a purpose and loving what you do." I was proud of myself, thinking I already knew what she was going to say this time.

"Good. But there's a third element. Do you remember that we were going to talk about Effortless Energy at the mental level?" She asked.

"Yes, I remember something. I've never heard any reference to Effortless Energy from any of the crew," I said.

"You're right. That's because they don't know the teaching intellectually, they embody it in their actions. I came here today to share this teaching with you. If you can master this one, you will take an important step towards greater freedom. Are you back in the world of the conscious?"

I changed positions so that I was propped up on my elbows. "Lay it on me."

"We'll be using the same Medicine Wheel teaching symbol we used before. This time it is called the Wheel of Soft Power, or Wheel of Effortless Energy. Why don't you draw the symbol in the sand."

I looked around and my eyes rested on a large black raven feather lying near me. Strange, I hadn't seen it before. I rolled over to reach it and then drew a large circle in front of me.

She watched. "Good. Keep in mind the Wheel is divided into nine sections: one for each of the cardinal directions of North, South, East, West; the non-cardinal directions of Northeast, Southeast, Southwest, and Northwest; and one for the Center. Each place represents different things, which vary among the tribes. It's not important for our purposes to go into those differences now. Also, this is not a linear teaching, but it is best to present it in a certain order. Just know that all things are going on simultaneously." I wasn't sure what all that meant, but I nodded, and she went on.

"The South, or the bottom of the circle, represents 'The End of Sacrifice.' In the West, or to your left, you have 'Foreknowing;' in the North, at the top of the circle is 'Alignment;' and in the East, or to your right, you have 'Release the Expected, and Embrace the Unexpected.' Now close your eyes and visualize this wheel. Can you see it?" She had closed her eyes and raised her face to the blue sky. She was motionless, concentrating.

"Yes. But how am I going to remember all this? I don't have anything to write on." I said, concerned she was going too fast.

She opened her eyes and looked directly into mine. "You will remember. As I speak this, it will become imprinted in your memory. Do not think about it, do not worry about forgetting anything. Just take it in. First I will describe what each direction means. Then I will go back and expand on each in more detail." Somehow, I didn't doubt what she said. I tried to relax.

"The South is the place of emotions, and the child in trust and innocence. One of the most significant ways in which humans have sacrificed at an emotional level is in not being given, and not giving yourselves, permission to be who you really are. We talked about this as part of the Puzzle Theory."

"I remember," I said as I leaned back on my elbows again.

"Throughout your history your women have often sacrificed significant aspects of who they are because your patriarchal rulers ordained them to be only wives and mothers. If a woman wanted to express her creativity outside of, or in addition to, being a wife and mother, she was discouraged or forbidden through lack of support, ostracism, ridicule, or even physical punishment. The same system forced your men to deny significant aspects of who they are, especially at the emotional and feeling level. Growing up did you ever hear, 'Big boys don't cry.' 'Don't let them see you sweat.' 'Keep your feelings to yourself.' Sound familiar?" she asked.

"Yep. I remember my father as a very loving man who rarely showed his feelings. I only recall him showing sadness one time, and that was when his father died. I was only five years old, but I remember it seeming so unusual to see my father sad. But I'm not clear on the sacrifice." I said.

"The sacrifice is living the picture on the outside of the box, consciously or unconsciously. It's what you do to yourself when you don't express fully who you are. It is a tremendous sacrifice for women to deny their creative expression, and just as big a sacrifice for men to stuff their feelings. It causes low self esteem, a feeling of powerlessness, and physical and emotional dis-ease."

I squinted, looking up at the sun. "I'm not sure I see the connection."

"Patience. In the West, is Foreknowing. This means having the ability to tap into what I call Environmental Cues: information that is constantly around us and within us. Information we can use to get in touch with who we are, what we want. Our task is to become aware of those Environmental Cues and come into alignment with them. Alignment is what the North is teaching us. Once we recognize the information, we can honor it and align with it." As she talked I had been stroking the raven feather. She paused.

I looked up at her. "And the East?" I asked.

"While all directions are important and powerful, the East is the one with which many have difficulty. The East is the place where you must Release the Expected and Embrace the Unexpected. The pictures on your box lead to certain expectations. You have learned to expect someone to take care of you, to provide a job no matter how you perform, to be there when you need them. You expect to live a long life, to not have illness, to not be injured. You expect the electricity to always be on, the phone to work, the television to entertain, your politicians and leaders to be truthful, etc. And, you're often disappointed."

"You're right, we do have a lot of expectations. No wonder we're disappointed so often." I said.

She nodded, "Yes, then there are all those expectations others have of you—your parents, spouse, children, friends, boss, the government. Everybody has a picture on their box of how life should be. And it often conflicts with how you would like your life to be. That's why the East is so important, and so difficult. The solution is simple, but not easy."

"Why does that not surprise me? I can already tell you are teaching me something that is very difficult to attain. I don't know anybody who regularly lives life this way. How can I do something no one else seems to be able to do?"

"You are limiting your thinking, Charly. First, many people consciously or unconsciously know this teaching and are living it. You have witnessed the guides recognizing Environmental Cues here in the Canyon and aligning themselves with natural rhythms to make their jobs easier. You have learned that Marian recognized the sacrifices she was making in the business world, and how she began following her gut feelings when she became a guide. The list goes on. Second, you have nothing to learn. This is about becoming aware, waking up to what is already natural. That is why the Grand Canyon is such a wonderful place to learn. You become aware of what is natural, and you see by comparison what you have allowed to become normal in your life."

"Well, how do I do it? How do I change things?" I said, frustration straining my voice. She was giving me information, but no answers.

"By remembering. Remembering what you have forgotten. That's what learning is. Educate comes from the Latin word *educare* which means 'pulling out that which is within.' You already know this. It is inside your box, at the feeling level. All you have to do is be willing to access it and have the courage to act on it."

Again the feelings of frustration began rising in my belly. I heard what she was telling me, and it made sense. It really felt right, but it was so far beyond anything I had learned or done in my life that it seemed beyond my reach.

"I can't handle this, Spirit Dancer. I'm confused and frustrated." My voice trailed off.

"Well, at least you're telling the truth about how you're feeling. It is, however, a misinterpretation of your feeling that I am compelled to correct. You are allowing fear to rule. Right now I want you to walk around the Wheel. See this from another direction. What else could your feelings be telling you?"

A few moments later, I still hadn't spoken. She walked over and took the feather from my hand. Held it to the sun and began examining it. "Take all the time you need. We're not going anywhere for awhile."

The patience in her voice had a calming effect on me. I closed my eyes, drew my knees to my chest and slowly rocked back and forth. I tried to come up with a different interpretation of this feeling.

She lowered the feather and began stroking it lovingly as I had. "Go where the feelings are in your body. Ask what it is feeling."

"I don't understand. Ask my body to talk to me? This is really absurd." My discomfort was making me testy.

"It's not absurd at all. Your body knows far more than you think. It is designed to provide you with instantaneous feedback. Where in your body are you feeling either tightness or the sensation you called confusion and frustration?"

My hand went immediately to my stomach. "In my gut, right below my diaphragm."

"Excellent. Now focus on that area only. Ask it what is the emotion—mad, sad, glad, or scared?" She used the feather to point at her own stomach.

After a second I said. "Hmmm. Scared and sad, I think."

Her voice became very quiet. "Good, very good. Now ask that same sensation what it needs."

My mind was blank. I sat for a long time and got nothing but more frustration. It was obvious I was having trouble.

She sat back down. "You're trying too hard. Just relax. Take a deep breath, focus on the sensation, and ask again what it is trying to tell you, what is the sadness all about?"

I did as she suggested, and heard some words. "I think I'm afraid that I won't be able to change my life, and at the same time I fear that I will be able to change, but I don't know where those changes might take me. I think it's fear of the unknown also."

"Now ask it what it needs. And don't be attached to the answer. Just let it come," she said.

I took a deep breath, trying to focus. I relaxed a little, and suddenly a voice inside me said, "you must stop lying about who you are."

Spirit Dancer was staring straight at me. "What the hell does that mean?" I said.

"It is how you end sacrifice, Charly. By having the courage to tell the truth from your heart. Heart in French is coeur, thus courage. You have been lying all your life, Charly, as have most humans. In fact, everyone else."

"How can you make a blanket statement like that? It's ridiculous," I said.

"Is it? Let me ask you this. Do you know anyone who has told a white lie?" She was on her feet again. A breeze had come up and moved the white robe. It felt good.

"Yes." I said, a little defensively.

"That's a lie. How about anyone who has told a half truth?" She didn't wait for my answer, but went on. "That's a lie. What about anyone who has withheld the truth for fear of hurting someone, usually himself?"

This time her gaze fell on me. "Yes," I said.

"That's a lie, too. How about anyone who has not asked for what they wanted, and settled for far less, or worse what they didn't want?" She waited for my answer, staring.

"Everybody. Okay, I surrender. So what's the way out of sacrifice, again?" I asked.

"Having the courage to tell the truth from your heart. Remember the motto, if you can't say 'Hell Yes!', say 'No.'"

I nodded thinking how many times I'd wanted to say 'Hell No.'

"Living your truth from your heart, giving with the heart. No obligation, no deceit, just giving without strings, or not giving, as the case may be. That is truly the beginning, both of ending sacrifice and becoming more free. Knowing yourself well enough to know and speak the truth."

"Let me continue," she said, "To access Environmental Cues, you must become quiet enough to receive them. This means slowing down, quieting the mind, so that you can hear Yahoo, your inner wisdom, which is constantly speaking to you between your thoughts. Environmental Cues come in many forms, all of which provide information that is helpful. They come from nature, as you have seen here in the Canyon. They come in the form of reflections from others, like your tyrants, like Frank. Also as intuitive or instinctive hits, your gut feelings. If you listen to your body, you will hear most of what you need."

I listened to my body, and it needed to move. I stood and stretched with my arms overhead without saying anything.

She continued. "Once you hear the cue, then you must come into alignment with it. This requires discipline. It is difficult enough to notice the cue. Living in such a busy, noisy world makes it even more challenging to align with it."

I stopped stretching. "You can say that again."

"I see a furrowed brow. Let me give you an example," she said.

"Thank you. I'm starting to get overwhelmed." I twisted left to right from the waist.

"Just take a couple of deep breaths. You're doing fine. Now, have you ever been driving in your car and sensed something about to happen with no apparent evidence to back you up?" Her head tilted to the left to get my reaction.

"Sure. Many times." I said, bending to touch my toes.

"What did you do with the information?" I turned my head from my bent position to see her bending too and looking at me.

We came up at the same time. "Usually nothing. Maybe look around more carefully."

"That is a beginning. Let's say your instincts told you there may be a car coming from your right through the next intersection. Aligning with this Environmental Cue would mean taking your foot off the accelerator, getting ready to hit the brakes in case there was a car there. You have nothing to lose by doing this, except a few seconds of time. It could save your life, or that of a loved one. Under-stand?" She turned and walked a few steps toward the river.

"I do. And I can think of times when I have actually done that and there was a car coming. But I never thought...." I hesitated.

"As I said, you already know this. It is merely becoming more conscious, more of the time. Pulling out that which is within." I was listening. "Now to the East. To release the expected and embrace the unexpected requires two things that are by any defini-tion underdeveloped in most humans. Be present, and be trusting. As that great shaman, Socrates, in The Way of the Peaceful Warrior says, 'There is only one time and only one place we can be, and that is here and now.' Being present is usually where you are not. You are either in the future with fear, worry, and expectations, or in the past with guilt and wishing you could do something over. To be in the here and now, to be able to embrace the unexpected, you must mas-ter the Art of Trust."

My body felt better, and I was able to better focus my atten-tion. "How do I do that?" I asked.

"Begin simply with the intention to be trusting. Every time you feel you might be analyzing something too much, force yourself to stop and feel. When your thoughts are interrupted by a strong sen-sation, don't force the feelings aside, pay attention to them. You need do nothing else. Just focus on trusting yourself, your instincts."

"This is all pretty abstract. How do I know when I'm not trusting?" My skepticism was kicking in again.

"If you are trusting, you are fully in the present moment. If you are impatient, it is evidence of the presence of fear, and you are in the future or the past. Impatience is the signal you are not trusting."

"I hear some of your group approaching. This is a good place to stop. Everything we've discussed is on the Wheel of Effortless Energy. Use your time in the Canyon to practice, while you're not as distracted by the speed of life. You will remember this. Practice makes perfect, Charly. Enjoy."

At that moment a group emerged from behind the mesquite trees. Marian was in the lead. "Talking to yourself, Charly?" she said with a smile.

I turned and looked toward the river. Spirit Dancer was still visible, but as apparent as she was to me, evidently Marian and the others could not see her. Spirit Dancer turned and started walking up stream.

As I stared after her, I absent mindedly said, "First signs of senility, I guess."

Spirit Dancer turned and the last thing I saw before she was completely gone was a smile on her face, showing she was enjoying my discomfort. Marian just gave me a strange look and was then distracted by the arrival of several others.

In a few minutes, everybody was climbing the boulder I'd used as my diving board, and jumping into the pool. There was a lot of dunking and splashing. Everyone enjoyed the warmer waters. It was a very playful group that headed back to the boats. Several others had noted the same boulder chute that I had on my way up. We all stopped at the slide and Dean and Marian showed us how to put our life jackets on like diapers. Turning our life jackets upside down, stepping through the armholes and pulling them into our crotches, we then clipped them so they fit snugly. The padding would protect our backsides, especially vulnerable tailbones, from any lurking rocks. The guides then walked, or should I say waddled, to the edge of the river. We quickly followed, like baby ducklings lined up behind Mom.

One by on we jumped into the river and floated down through the slide. Then someone had another idea, and at one point we all linked up and made a long snake. Twelve adults were screeching like ten-year-olds, and having a ball. No one wanted to leave and head for the boats, but we were getting hungry.

As I walked back, the thought struck me, "Why is it that as adults we lose that spontaneity we had as kids?" Obviously it's still there, and just needs the opportunity and the inspiration to surface. I made a vow to include that as one of the things I would change in my life. I was going to play more. I felt Spirit Dancer would approve.

On the way back to the rafts, the beauty of the Canyon again stood out. The incredible shade of blue in the Little Colorado flowed directly toward Chuar Butte, a prominent Canyon feature directly across from the Little "C". The butte was framed by a deep desert blue sky streaked with the soft brush strokes of high cirrus clouds. Another unparalleled mural for the mind.

We'd spent more time playing at the Little "C" than planned, so Greg decided to go to the first available camp site, which happened to be just around the corner. Floating out of the Little Colorado we again entered the cold, green surge of the Big Colorado. For several hundred yards the blue and green ran side by side, warm water resisting being swallowed up by the cold. Eventually their marriage would change the deep green into a more opaque shade.

Dinner was prepared quickly and devoured even faster by a tired group of happy campers. As we ate, Greg told us our current camp had been named Crash Camp to mark the June 30, 1956 collision high above of two commercial airliners. The collision had claimed the lives of 128 passengers and crew. At the time it was the largest disaster in commercial airline history. Not a real pleasant thought, but it wasn't dwelt on.

Next we went over the plan for tomorrow. We would be getting on the river a little earlier than usual. It would be the longest river day thus far, 26 miles, and Greg said if we didn't get a lot of wind, we would still be able to take a hike. I heard something about big water, but my mind drifted off, more interested in what was becoming a daily feature, a beautiful sunset of pink, fuscia and soft orange designed to calm the soul and still the mind. Canyon sunsets are often subtle, since we only see the very top of the sky, but this one was striking.

As I lay in my bag feeling the soft breeze off the river, I marveled at how comfortable I felt. I watched a large moon rise. Even though it was several days from full, it lit up the Canyon walls, revealing infinitely varied shapes and figures in its shadows. "Life is a perceptual experience," I heard in my mind, as I began my journey to the Fifth Dimension. And we choose the perception.

Chapter Eleven

Shifting Perceptions

At the sound of the first conch shell, I rolled over and looked up to see threatening clouds. There would be no mountains burning golden in the sky this morning. True to his word, Greg was all business. Breakfast consisted of oatmeal and bagels, which were prepared and eaten quickly. We cleaned up and loaded everything on the rafts and shoved off around 7:30. There was no wind, but I could tell the guides were anticipating something. They were more business-like than usual, and had made extra efforts when tying in the black bags and equipment.

When I asked James about it, he said we would be running some major rapids and the guides always "rig for flipping." As he said it, I remembered hearing Greg talk about "big water" last night while I was preoccupied with the sunset. Hearing the words "flipping" now, made me nervous.

Knowing that we would encounter a number of rapids, and because of the cloudy skies, most everyone had prepared for the day by having rain gear close at hand. It wasn't long before we were scrambling to get it on. Not because of rapids, but because a light mist was falling and clinging to everything. This was nothing compared to the rain that had come in sheets and torrents with the wind on the second day. Actually, this added an intriguing element to the Canyon. It softened everything. There was no harsh contrast of dark and light, and clouds hovered around the rim. The Canyon was pulling in, and we were being pulled in as a result. The rafts ran closer together, and our focus had narrowed to getting through each rapid safely.

We hadn't gone too far when Wally gave a signal and all the boats rendezvoused while we received a lecture on a geological phenomenon known as an unconformity. This occurs when two rock layers are not contiguous in time. In this case there was the Dox Sandstone on the bottom, formed about 1.1 billion years ago. Immediately on top is the Tapeats Sandstone, formed 570 million years ago. Where those two formations touch is 540 million years of missing earth history.

"How can that much rock be missing?" I asked Wally .

"During that half a billion years, there was tremendous earth activity. Earthquakes, volcanic eruptions, rock layers being pushed up as much as two, three miles to form an alpine mountain range. Oceans advanced and left deposits of limestone, sandstone and shale, and followed by long periods of erosion. Most of the soft rock formed during that time period eroded, eaten away before the Tapeats Sea came in and deposited the sandstone you see there," he said pointing to the rock at the river level.

"It's really hard to grasp that much time," commented Jane.

"I have a simple way to explain all this activity," James offered.

"Great, that's what I need. Simple explanations for a simple mind," I said.

"Think about the earth history of the Grand Canyon as a huge book. Each page in the book represents one year of history. Page one was written one billion 700 million years ago. That's the age we give the oldest rock in the Canyon. The last page in the book is this year."

"Wow, mind boggling. That's a lot of pages," interjected Richard.

Jane agreed by nodding her head and raising her eyebrows.

I glanced in Frank's direction expecting some type of rhetorical comment from him, but he just sat huddled in his rain gear, hood pulled up trying to avoid the wet mist.

James continued, "The higher the rock formation in the Canyon, the younger it is. The lower the formation, the older it is. Geologists call this phenomena superposition, with younger rock above older rock. So the Dox Sandstone formed somewhere towards the beginning of the book, 1.1 and 1.2 billion years ago. After that, many more pages were written in the form of other rock layers. Now, Wally mentioned that much of the soft rock eroded during that time period. So, imagine pages representing 1.1 billion to 570 million were written, and then those same pages were torn out, eroded. Then the Tapeats Sea advanced 570 million years ago, and for the next 10 million years or so, laid down the sandstone that we call Tapeats. Between the Tapeats and Dox Sandstone pages, there were at one time 540 million pages of earth history, written and then torn out. Does that make sense?"

"Yeah. Its easy to follow it that way. I wonder if they recycled," I jested.

"Everything in nature is recycled, Charly. So your attempt at humor is also correct. Whenever rock erodes, it gets carried by wind and water towards the ocean, where it gets deposited and eventually becomes rock again. In a way that is the purpose of rocks. To travel from its high points in the mountains and high desert toward bodies of water like the Pacific and Atlantic Oceans, the Caribbean, and the Sea of Cortez in the Gulf of California. Over time, the eroded particles become cemented together, lithified, into rocks. And a new cycle is born."

"Yeah, I know. Death gives life, etcetera," I trailed off thinking of Spirit Dancer's poem.

"What?" James replied with a blank look on his face.

"Oh, just something I heard one time," I said. The thought stayed with me that everything on earth, even the people, are actually recycled.

During the rest of the morning we were in the widest section of the Canyon thus far. Known as the Palisades of the Desert, the widening was due to the erosion of the Dox Sandstone and other rock layers which caused the Canyon walls above them to recede from the river.

We were approaching Unkar Delta. On the river map it is a huge point jutting out forming a very sharp "S" turn in the river. Across from the Delta is Unkar Rapid, a medium-sized rapid that runs right alongside the rock wall. It was dwarfed by a sheer cliff rising straight out of the river. We had originally planned on stopping to visit the ruins of the largest exposed habitation site in the Canyon, but Greg decided to cover as many miles as possible early in the day, in case the winds should pick up later. The mist continued and the weather forecast for the rest of the day was still a mystery.

As we continued our float past the Delta rising above on the river's right side, my imagination returned to what it would have been like living in the Canyon in prehistoric times. I asked James to tell me what he knew about the Unkar Delta inhabitants.

"Well, they were the Anasazi, as you know. Historians believe habitation began around 850 AD, peaked around 1100 AD and the site was abandoned by 1250 AD for reasons not fully understood. Many feel the people moved on because of a sustained drought. Others think maybe they left because of some type of enemy invasion. Whatever happened, archaeologists note four distinct eras from hunter-gatherers to farming and sophisticated pottery making. The farming included squash, beans, and corn. They also ate meat from rabbits and big horn sheep, and gathered beans from mesquite trees. Their diet was supplemented with fruit, such as prickly pear, and seeds. During one period, evidence indicates they lived in pueblo-like apartment buildings, and what you would have seen if you had gone to shore would have been the remains of the foundations. They look like what we would call row houses. Two to seven rooms faced a subterranean ceremonial room called a kiva, a large sunken circle."

"They sure must have been an energetic lot. That trail leading up to the granaries was amazing," I said.

"They did what they had to for survival, and when it got too much for them, they left," replied James.

We ran a couple of fun rapids including Nevills, the biggest one to date, and then came around a bend where the Canyon again narrowed. The current suddenly slowed to a crawl and we all relaxed. But not for long. Downstream, I began to hear a low ominous growl. My gut tightened as the volume increased. The tremendous roar I had heard on the first day while approaching Badger sounded like a cat's meow, compared to what I was hearing now. I flipped through my River Guide book.

"Hance?" I asked, looking at James.

"Hance," he replied. "We'll be scouting this one."

I wondered when we would pull over. We floated very close to the beginning of the rapid before moving toward the south shore. Too close, as far as I was concerned. Knowing that James was a trainee added to my insecurity.

On shore the crew began a trek up a sandy trail to a viewing point high above the rapid. I was feeling too weak to go there, so I stopped below them and found a rock to sit on. I grasped the rock and it occurred to me that rocks are great symbols of security and protection. I wanted all the security I could get right now. I held on.

From my vantage point, there was no way we were getting through this rapid safely. I looked up to see the guides gesturing towards the river as they talked to each other. There must be a difference of opinion. The roar was deafening. The longer I waited, the more scared I became. I became aware of a moist feeling and looked around to see if the mist had started again. Then I realized the moist feeling wasn't outside my rain gear, it was inside. I was sweating profusely, even in the cloudy, cool weather.

The sound reminded me of an earthquake I thought I was in years ago. I had been in southern Illinois hitchhiking. When the driver pulled over to sleep after two days, I threw my sleeping bag under a bush and crawled in exhausted. I was almost asleep when I felt the ground shake and heard a deep rumble. Earthquake! It had to be an earthquake! I sat up in my bag in time to see the bright headlight of a freight train flash by. Turns out, the bush I was under was only fifteen feet from the railroad tracks. I half laughed to myself about how scared I'd been then, and some of my tension subsided. Even so, I was still an ashen color of gray, when James passed by my rock. He sensed my nervousness and pulled me aside, issuing an invitation that led to a remarkable shift in me.

"Charly, this is the most technical rapid in the Canyon at this low water level," he began. "I could use your help in getting through safely. Will you do that?"

"How?" I asked, not having any idea how to read the river. This guy must really be desperate, asking me for help.

"Well, we've all discussed it and there are a lot of 'markers' in this rapid. Rocks, holes and waves that I need to keep track of. If I show you the run, you could help me keep track of where we are. What do you say?"

"If you think I can help, I'll give it a shot," I said. To myself I thought, 'Better than sitting around waiting for the worst.'

"Great," he said, hitting me on the shoulder. We moved back over and climbed onto the rock where I'd been sitting. He began pointing toward Hance. "So we're going to enter on the left side of the tongue over there in the right center of the river. Then we have to go between two rocks, miss a pourover on the right." Looking over at me he said, "That's where water runs over a rock and forms a trench behind."

I nodded and he continued, waving at the river again. "Then there's a hole on the left, which is similar to a pourover, beyond that we need to grab some slack water, move left, and miss some rocks. We'll have to hit some big waves in the middle straight on, find a slot between two big holes, and hit some more big waves. Follow that?"

"Are you kidding? One more time. Let me study it for a couple minutes," I said overwhelmed.

"Take as much time as you need." He went over it again, then said, "Now close your eyes and see if you can picture the whole run. I'm going to head back to the boat and make sure everything is tied down."

I looked closely at the line he had described, then did as he said with the visualization. By the time I got back to the boat, I was feeling much better. I'd stopped to drain my bladder, which seemed to fill up despite my sweaty condition and without drinking any more water. The other boats were pulling out.

"Okay, let's get out of here," I said to James. He tied up the bow line, reminded me to tightened my life jacket, and shoved off.

Rapids are formed because debris gets imposed into the river, usually from a flash flood originating from a side canyon. The result is a mini-dam, backing the water up and slowing it down.

It seemed to take us a long time to reach the head of the rapid, but then I could see down its entire length. I was glad James had included me, because if he hadn't, I would have been terrified at this point. Instead, I was excited. Without thinking I stood up in the front of the boat, and while holding on tightly to the safety lines, heard myself yelling encouragement and directions to James. The rapid was so raucous he probably couldn't hear a word I said, but I was so pumped, I didn't care.

"There you go, James, you're right on track. There's the entry. Yes! Good going, right between the rocks. Wow, look at the size of that hole! Glad you missed that one. There's the slack water. James, get a little more left." I waved frantically. "Rock ahead, more left! Yes! Big waves, James, hit 'em straight! Where's that slot. I don't see it. God, these waves are twice as big as they appeared from shore. There! Move right James. The slot is farther right! Yeah! Oh my God, look at the size of . . . ! Boy, glad you hit those monsters straight. Great ruuuunnnn, James!"

I was jumping around like a wild man. He sat in the middle of the boat stunned, finally exhaling in relief, he let out a whoop. "Best run I ever had in Hance, Charly. Couldn't hear much of what you said, but it must have worked. Good to have you along."

"Thanks, especially for showing me the way. Until you did that, I was convinced we were going to die. I couldn't see any way through. It was fun, and I'm shocked I'm even saying that. In thirty seconds I went from the brink of death to sheer exhilaration. What a rush!" I drank a whole quart of water to lubricate my mouth which had enough cotton in it to make a shirt, and then fell back and listened to my heart return to normal.

We ran another big rapid called Sockdolager, which was fun, but had none of the terror I had felt at Hance. I thought about my attitude shift, and realized it was from the information and invitation by James. The information helped me see we could make it. The invitation allowed me to participate, to make a contribution, even though it was relatively small. I was involved, and it was far better than being a passive spectator hoping for a safe outcome.

I thought about some of my past work experiences, and how much better my job perception and my performance would have been had my bosses been more generous with their information, and had they allowed us to get involved in decision making processes. After all, the employees were closer to the day-to-day problems than they were. We could have come up with some dynamite solutions if we'd been asked.

The river was starting to mellow out, and we were in a spectacular part of the Canyon. The Inner Gorge had begun just below Hance, and the rock formations appeared to be different than any others we had seen.

James told me the rock was metamorphic Vishnu Schist. He described the rock as the roots of a giant tooth, the tooth being two 14,000 to 18,000 foot Alpine mountain ranges that had formed and eroded, eventually revealing the schist underneath. Originally the schist had been limestone, sandstone, and shale lying on the bottom of an ancient ocean. Movement in the earth's surface folded the ocean bottom rocks together and pushed them, accordion-like, deeper into the earth. There they were subjected to the intense pressure of the mountains forming above them, and the heat of the molten rock, called magma, that lies below.

The rock was dark and iridescent, rising straight out of the river, narrowing the channel and causing a closed-in feeling. The schist reminded me of something I might see in a Ralph Bakshi animated cartoon set in medieval days. The dark, threatening clouds hanging over us, like Snoopy hovering over his empty food dish, only added to the atmosphere.

James roused me from my musings, "When Major John Wesley Powell came down here on his first exploration in 1869, he made a note after leaving Marble Canyon. He said, 'Hard rocks make hard rapids,' and he wrote these classic lines in his journal." James paused his rowing and took on a dramatic expression. "We are about to enter the great unknown. We have an unknown distance yet to run, an unknown river to explore. What falls there are we know not. What rocks beset the channel, we know not. What walls rise above the Canyon, we know not. Ahh well! We may conjecture many things. The men talk as cheerfully as ever. Jests are bandied about freely this morning, but to me the cheer is somber and the jests are ghastly.'" He finished with much emphasis on ghastly.

"Well, I'll have to admit I'm glad to be here in the Canyon with all of you guys, knowing you've been down here numerous times," I said.

"You mean someone told you I'd done this before? No, this is my first time," he said.

I looked up startled, then realized he was pulling my leg.

We floated past Clear Creek, where we were hoping to hike. Greg told us we weren't going to do that because the threat of rain made the hike too risky. The mist was gone, but the clouds still looked ominous. Instead we pulled over just below Clear Creek at a camp called Zoroaster, ate a leisurely lunch, and swapped tales of running Hance and Sockdolager. If I hadn't been present in the run myself, I'd have bet the stories were like fish stories, because Hance seemed to get bigger in every telling.

Dean then gave us a lecture about the Inner Gorge, the schist and the bands of granite that had been injected into the schist from some magma chamber deep in the earth. He also talked about contact metamorphism, which sounded like a disease to me, but turns out to be the result of heated rock, like molten granite, making contact with other rock.

Just below Hance and high up on the rocks, there appeared to be an unnatural opening of some kind. Jane asked what it was and Marian told us it was an old asbestos mine that had been exploited by John Hance, the rapid's namesake. John had been the first permanent settler on the South Rim, as well as a prospector and entrepreneur. Dean chimed back in to tell us that asbestos is an example of contact metamorphism. In this case, lava made contact with a formation known as Bass Limestone. The asbestos was the result of the heat changing the crystalline structure of the limestone. It turns out that the value of asbestos is directly proportional to the length of its fibers. Even though the rock in which it forms is hard, miners can't use dynamite because it would destroy the fibers. So asbestos must be mined by hand. He also mentioned there are only two countries in the world that currently mine asbestos, Canada and Korea.

After lunch, we were actually only a few miles from our camp for the evening, and we floated that distance very leisurely. I don't think James took more than three or four swipes with the oars, and then only to stay out of an eddy. Greg's raft pulled along side of ours. I heard that this camp was called Cremation because it was near Cremation Creek. I was afraid to ask why it was called Cremation Creek. I didn't need to hear a horror story. Frank, on the other hand, blurted out the question.

Dean volunteered the information. Apparently it was aptly named because it is in the sun from early till late in the day. In the summer, it is unwise to show up before late afternoon because "the sun is so hot you'll . . . " He wasn't allowed to finish, because we all added simultaneously, "be cremated."

The feeling around camp was different, not only because we had just run the biggest water so far, but due to the imminent departure of the passengers who had only signed on for the six-day trip. This included Richard, whom many of us had come to love. During dinner, Greg discussed the logistics for those hiking out. We would be getting up early again and Dean would leave right after breakfast with Richard and the others who were hiking out. They would be dropped at Pipe Creek Beach, mile 89, where they would begin their seven and a half mile hike out of the Canyon. Greg reminded them that the elevation change is 4,600 feet, making it very challenging.

Richard groaned out loud, but then he winked at me and I was reminded of his new determination to keep going whenever he felt like quitting. I knew that even in his overweight condition, he would make it.

The rest of us would float a quarter mile to Phantom Ranch. The so-called Ranch is the only place in Grand Canyon at the river level with man-made structures. It's up the Bright Angel Creek about a quarter of a mile, and is a cluster of stone and wood cabins, dormitories for hikers who must make reservations well in advance, and a dining hall. It was constructed in 1922 as a rest stop for tourists by Fred Harvey, a park concessionaire.

There we would pick up any mail that was waiting for the crew, and the duffel bags for the passengers that would be joining us. The passengers would have hiked down that day, and the mail would have been brought down by mule.

It was strange thinking about Richard and the others leaving after having shared so much with them. It was even harder thinking about four new people that we didn't know starting in the middle of the trip.

Greg asked any of those leaving if they wanted to say anything. After some hesitation, each one said a few words about their experience, and what meaning it had for them. It was evident that all were sad to be leaving. One said she signed up for six days because she didn't want to be trapped for two weeks if she didn't like it. She admitted now that it had been an unwise decision, but she declared, "I'll be back."

Then Richard stood up, his ample belly jiggling, sweat beading on his forehead, a gentle smile on his lips. "When I signed up for this trip, it was a real stretch. After five days, it still is," he began, his face lighting up with a smile as everyone laughed. "I'm 43 and have never done anything like this in my life. I had no idea what it meant to sleep in a tent, let alone under the stars. I envisioned lying awake all night, worried about snakes or bears." Again everyone erupted in laughter, but it was with him not at him. He went on, "When I stepped off the bus at Lees Ferry, I immediately went down to the river and walked in. I thought it would be warm, like one of the shallow rivers in Michigan. You know what I mean, Charly," he glanced my way.

I nodded. He went on sharing his feelings. "The shock of that 45 degree water took away all my anxiety. Something about this place was comforting to me, even before we began. I have never slept as well as I have down here. I can't believe how easily I've fit in." He paused, tears welling in his eyes. "I have no doubt the hike out tomorrow is going to be the hardest thing I've ever done physically. When I get to the top I'll probably collapse, so I hope one of you will be there to pick me up. Fortunately, the hike to the ruins at Nankoweap taught me something I'll never forget, and will put to use tomorrow. Halfway up the trail, I was out of breath and out of energy. I looked up to the granaries and thought, there is no way, it's just not worth it. But just then Frank came by huffing and puffing, and I thought, by God, if he can do this so can I. So I got off my butt and kept going."

Frank looked a little embarrassed, but then proud that he had given someone incentive to realize a goal. He gave Richard a little wave.

Richard continued, "When I got to the top, most of you were already starting to head down. I looked around me and saw that amazing view downstream with the Canyon walls glowing and all I could think was, 'God, I'm glad I kept going.' It was worth every bit of the effort. I'm going to keep reminding myself of that as I hike tomorrow, and any other time when I think it's not worth the effort." He started to sit and then added one more statement that came out rather choked, "I want to . . . thank you for being a part of my wonderful memory."

He then walked over to each person, and one by one gave us a very loving hug. We had all been moved by Richard's words and it was a great way to bring an end to a long and eventful day.

Chapter Twelve

Big
Water

During the night, I had a dream. When I awoke in the morning, I lay motionless for a moment trying to recall what it was about. All I could remember were the words "conscious transition." Spirit Dancer was giving me another message, but it would have to wait until she showed up, or I became more skilled at remembering my dreams.

Camp was a flurry of activity. The four passengers hiking out had retrieved their back packs and were stuffing their personal gear inside. They had already made a lunch for themselves—sandwiches, fruit, nuts, and granola bars. Marian checked them for blisters, which she taped, and talked to them about drinking plenty of water and taking their time getting out. Richard said the latter would be no problem for him.

The hikers piled on Dean's boat and were given a rousing send-off and lots of good lucks. The rest of us ate breakfast, happy to be entertaining a more leisurely pace, but already feeling the separation from those leaving. We set about breaking down camp and loading the remaining boats.

Phantom beach was just around the bend. When we got there, Greg took off to call the office to check on the new passengers that were coming down, and to report on the progress of the first half of our trip. Wally ran up to Phantom Ranch, about a quarter mile off the river, to pick up mail. Marian and I found the incoming duffels at the hitching post near the beach, and carried them back to the boats. Others relaxed in the shade, or carried empty five gallon water jugs up to a hose for filling.

Not wanting to interrupt the flow of the trip, Greg said we would be there for as short a time as possible. While we waited, Jane and I talked about those hiking out, hoping they would be okay, especially Richard.

Jane was also very curious about the new people. This was day six for all of us. We'd covered 88 river miles and had shared a lot. We felt we were now seasoned river rats, familiar with the rapids and the routine of camping and hiking. How would the new passengers fit in? They wouldn't have the luxury we had of going five days before running a major rapid. Looking at my River Guide, I told Jane that they would have the grand total of one mile and fifteen minutes to get ready for the first of four major rapids we would encounter today. A grand welcome. They would be tired, sore and without a clue. I was already feeling sorry for them.

My pity turned out to be needless. When we pulled into Pipe Creek Beach, they were looking fit and ready to roll. Their name was Chance. Jack, Fran, Jessie and Nathan. I took an immediate liking to Nathan, who, at age ten was small for his age, as I had been. Even though he looked younger than his ten years, there was something about him that exuded confidence. It turned out the Chances were from northern Montana, near the Bob Marshall Wilderness. We would soon discover that young Nathan and his sister, Jessie, were wilderness experts who would be showing us a thing or two.

Gear and passengers loaded, Greg called us together. "Your adrenaline will be pumping today. We'll be running four major rapids and a dozen other very large ones in a twenty-mile stretch. Are you ready?"

We all looked at each tentatively, but no one said a word.

Horn Creek was short, but very intense. The Chances were initiated and we were on our way. Granite was next and it was like no other rapid we had seen. Running alongside the right wall, it was incredibly fast with one huge wave after another coming from all directions. If there was a model for chaos, this would be it. How we made it through without flipping I will never know.

Next came Hermit. My boat for the day was Marian's, and she told us we would have ten waves, with the first five increasing in size and intensity. She said it was one of her favorite rapids, and guaranteed us the most exciting ride to date. She wasn't wrong. As we entered the rapid, I looked downstream counting the waves to check out the fifth and supposedly largest. It didn't appear to be anywhere near as significant as Hance or Granite.

We slid down the silky smooth tongue. I looked at Jane next to me, who was laughing and screaming at the same time. Her mouth was moving, but I couldn't hear her. The deafening roar of the rapid drowned out all other sound. We hit the first wave and were moving faster than I'd expected. In an instant we were on top of wave two, larger than one but no big deal. Wave three was impressive, but when we came over the top of three and slid down into the trough of four, I looked up and saw one of those surfer-delights, like the Pipeline monsters I'd seen in movies on Hawaii's North Shore. For a moment I thought I'd lost track. This had to be the infamous fifth wave.

"Is this number five?!" I turned around and shouted to Marian.

"Four!" she yelled back, her eyes focused straight ahead, and her arms and body thrusting the oars forward in an attempt to gain enough momentum to make it up and over this gigantic still-growing wave. We reached the peak and I felt like I was in a rocket going to the moon. But, then we were propelled down the back of four and into the deep trough of five.

I looked up and was totally stunned. Jane was completely white, absolutely no color in her face. In front of us was the grand-mother of all waves, a twenty-five foot wall of water rising up to strike us dead. I had seen water like this one other time, when I was in the Navy. We had experienced forty-foot seas, but I was in a 500 foot ship back then. Our little eighteen-foot raft seemed like a bathtub toy in a typhoon.

The immensity and intensity was impossible to believe. Even more impossible was believing we could make it through with-out getting annihilated. It was only a couple of seconds, but it felt like a slow-motion dream ride to a watery grave. We were suspended in time at the monster's mercy, and it teased us. We danced with it as it grew and we rose up its silky wall, but then it broke menacingly on top of us. For an instant we were motionless. Tons of icy water cascaded down on us.

Marian yelled, "High side!!" For a second I thought, "no way, I'm not letting go of this rope," but somehow I found myself beside Jane lunging forward to provide the additional weight needed to prevent an end over end flip. When the water receded from my eyes, there was Marian, right in the middle of the pile next to me. As she yelled, she'd also launched herself from her seat in the middle of the raft to add her weight as well. We emerged at the top of the wave, and for a picosecond I thought we were going to keep right on rising. There was that suspended-in-time-feeling again. Then the boat lost its balance, tipped forward, and we began the slide down the backside of the fifth wave. Somehow, Marian got back on her oars and was guiding us through tail waves that would have seemed big had we not just experienced number five.

The rafts began congregating at the bottom of the rapid. The guides were whooping and giving high-fives to their passengers, exchanging congratulations for their personal runs as well as for each other. Everyone was exuberant for one reason or another. Either it was mutual approval and respect for the power of the river, or for the skills of the guides, or for the fact that they were still alive. I wasn't sure about some of the passengers. For me, the exhilaration I felt was like none I had ever known. If it were physically possible, I would have carried the raft back upstream and run Hermit again and again.

"Okay everybody. We're far from through. There's more waiting downstream, so let's make miles." It was Greg, bringing us all back to the present reality. We had just begun. Boy, had we ever.

"I could do that run about a dozen more times," I said to no one in particular. "What's next, Marian?"

"Boucher, and then Crystal. After we get past Crystal, we'll run the Gems, a series of medium-high rapids that are named after gemstones. But, first we have to make it through Crystal." She spoke of Crystal with such respect that even with my veteran attitude, her tone of voice made my stomach jump.

"Is Crystal bigger than Hermit?" I asked a little cautiously.

"It's definitely one of the big ones," she replied noncommittally. "We'll stop and scout it before we run."

Now anxiety was creeping its way into my gut. Hance had been the only rapid we'd scouted so far. I masked my fear with another question.

"What's the story with Crystal?" I said, trying to sound casual.

Marian tucked her oar handles under her knees, and let the raft float in the current. She opened her personal ammo can and pulled out a map, laid it out and began to explain.

"This used to be a pretty calm stretch of the Inner Gorge. In December of 1966 that all changed." Pointing to the map, she went on. "That year there was quite a bit of snow on the North Rim, which is about 6,000 feet higher than the river and around 14 miles back. Over an eighteen hour period, it rained and caused the snow pack to begin melting. The trickles became torrents of water, converging above the Crystal drainage and cascading to the canyon floor, where they picked up steam and began carrying debris consisting of dirt, rocks and even boulders. Most people don't realize that as moving water's volume doubles which it was doing constantly, it's power quadruples. Before long this flood was carrying house-sized boulders towards the Colorado."

Looking at Jane, her eyes were as big as saucers, and I felt a little weak myself.

Whether Marian noticed or not, she kept going, "When the flood burst out of Crystal Canyon, it pushed everything into the Colorado River, forming a huge debris fan and pinching down the river. When the river is pinched down, the same volume of water has to flow through a narrower space, and so it has to speed up. The additional speed plus the huge boulders and other debris created a major rapid that is still unstable. That's why we scout it. It could have changed since we were here two weeks ago."

She refolded and replaced the map, and began rowing to catch the other boats.

Marian's description was so vivid I could imagine that torrent of rock, mud and water emerging from the side canyon. And it caused me to be curious about something she said. "If it's still changing and can do so that quickly, isn't it possible that it could eventually revert back to its more peaceful state?"

"It would have been possible before man entered the picture." Her voice was somewhat harsh.

"What has man to do with it?" Jane asked.

"The dam. See, before the dam at Glen Canyon, and all the other dams on the Colorado, the river had a natural cycle that included periodic flash floods of great magnitude. Those floods, often in Spring from annual snow melt, would come racing through the Canyon and scour it, laying down fresh sediment. If a big flood had blocked the Colorado with boulders and other debris, chances are the spring floods would be enough to blast through and carry most of the debris downstream. That can't happen now because the snow melt gets contained in Lake Powell behind Glen Canyon Dam, and the amount of water flushed through the dam isn't enough to move boulders out of the way. So it looks like we're stuck with it."

Marian stopped talking to focus on Boucher, and then we entered a very calm stretch.

"Welcome to Crystal lake," she said smiling. I looked around. It was quite ironic to be calling a stretch of the river a lake, but that was what it looked like.

"We call it a lake because the water upstream of major rapids pools up and the current slows down significantly. That's why the river is so glassy calm here. The calm before the storm, so to speak," she said laughing. My stomach rolled.

"That's what happened when we came around the corner above Hance," I thought.

We floated silently for about ten minutes, and the Canyon's beauty was awesome. It tried to lull me into what I knew was a false sense of security. The size or significance of a rapid is often communicated nonverbally by the guides. I wasn't the only one who was nervous. Not only do they put more attention into preparation, but they seem to pee more. This rapid must be huge, because I saw several of the guides relieving themselves three or four times. Before long we began to hear the well-known rumble.

The roar was increasing in intensity as we approached the head of the rapid, and we pulled over about a hundred yards above on the north side of the river. Considering the intensity of Hermit, everybody, even the passengers, followed Greg through a forest of sugar cane-like vegetation to the scouting location. The path had clearly been trod many times in this ritual of paying homage to the powerful rapid that lay patiently in wait for any guide who would take it for granted, or lose his or her concentration for the slightest instant.

The guides congregated near the river on large boulders. I wondered at the immense power of a flood that could carry these monsters many miles before dropping them. I watched Dean, Greg, James, Wally and Marian go through the ritual of stroking beards or chins with left arm folded under the right elbow, as they watched the currents. It must help them think better, I reasoned. Again there was a great deal of pointing and gesturing as they discussed the best possible route. At one point Dean picked up a large dead branch and heaved it into the river. We all watched as the branch swam into the current, picked up speed and then disappeared into a huge wave at the entry. I was transfixed, waiting for the branch to emerge. After several seconds someone yelled, "There it is," pointing to the misshapen branch some two hundred feet downstream.

I could see Wally shake his head and laugh. Fragments of the statement, "better not go in there," were heard. Wally seemed to be the master of understatement. I watched James engrossed in his own thoughts, a look of concern etched on his face. I empathized. He'd told me that he'd almost flipped in this rapid on his first try two years before. The memory was clearly returning.

Finally the guides huddled together, and placing their hands on top of each other in the center of the circle, began the finale to their tribal ritual. Beginning with a low voice, they raised their joined hands and the pitch in unison, cresting with a loud warrior-like shout that raised everyone's adrenaline level. Next were hugs and pats on the back and, "See you at the bottom, right side up," accompanied by thumbs-up hand gestures.

They began the walk back to the boats and the rest of us fell in silently behind. I couldn't help but think this line resembled a funeral procession. There were a few attempts at humor, but I realized it was probably to mask the nervousness. There was no doubt this rapid was being approached differently. It was, as Greg had explained, not a good place to flip. We were in a part of the Canyon with few eddies or beaches that could provide safe havens in the event of a boat overturning. The current was strong, making it more difficult to get out of the fifty degree water, which meant hypothermia was a real possibility. To compound matters, there were two sections to the long rapid separated by a very dangerous rock island. Any boat flipping in the upper section risked being drawn directly into the island.

From the beginning, it was obvious that Crystal was most definitely in control here. Marian's boat was running second, behind Greg. Then came James, Dean, and Wally . I watched Greg maintain his usual effortless stroke. He turned his boat to face backwards, allowing him more power to break through the strong current coming off the shore at the top of the rapid. Unlike many of the other rapids, if we ran this one correctly, we would stay dry, and it would feel anti-climactic after all the posturing, and sweating during the scout. But we hadn't made it yet.

As usual, Greg's entry was perfect and he steered his raft far away from the obstacles that threatened to eat anything that got near. We were now at the entry point. Marian's record of never flipping was not to be altered here. Like Greg, she was a master, putting her raft right where she wanted. I offered my congratulations.

"Great run, Marian. I don't think we took on any water." My relief was short lived. Looking back upstream, I saw James enter Crystal. He was farther out than either Greg or Marian. His raft was heavily laden with all our equipment, and seemed at the mercy of the powerful currents. He was using all his strength and leverage, but his efforts seemed futile. In a flash the front end of his raft reared up, lifted by some invisible, unimaginably strong force. The raft twisted in a death spiral, held for a brief moment sadistically providing us with a shred of hope, then continued on its certain path.

The sight of an overturned raft is shocking. More unsettling was the lack of any sign of James. Marian and Greg were already in motion, pulling as hard as possible to try to head off James's boat. It was headed straight for the rock island, a partially submerged mine- field of boulders in the middle of the river, and it was obvious no one would catch it. Greg indicated he would go down the left side of the island and yelled for Marian to go right.

While straining at the oars, she threw me a canvas bag with a loop of rope sticking out one end. "When you see James, hold on to that loop and when I tell you, throw the bag downstream and a lit- tle past him!"

"What do I do then?" I was trying hard to remember every- thing from the river rescue lesson Greg had given us the first day.

"Just throw it and then I'll take over. If we're past the island, you can take the oars, and I'll pull him in!"

"I don't see him anywhere!" My voice was near panic. "You don't suppose he's trapped under the boat!"

"God, I hope not," yelled Marian. "It's the worst place to be, especially with that island. It's a good thing the water's high." Her voice was straining, betraying the energy she was expending just try- ing to catch James's raft. We were about ten feet away, when James popped up from underneath his raft.

Marian's voice was commanding. "Get him out of the water! We have to get away from the island."

I called to James. "We have to get you out of the water."

He flashed a big grin, and swam over to me. I grabbed the shoulders of his life jacket, as we had been instructed in our safety talk, counted one, two, and on three lifted as James kicked his legs and pulled up on the safety line anchored to the boat. He came fly- ing out of the water as if catapulted by some unseen source, and he ended up sprawled on top of me in the bottom of the raft.

"We have to stop meeting like this," he said, his grin even bigger. "God, thanks for getting me out of there you guys."

Marian had no time for gratitude. She was again pulling her guts out to get away from the island. As I looked back, James's boat had entered the rock field. The water was high enough that it man- aged to float all the way through, but the behavior of the raft made it clear that the rocks were close enough to the surface to do great bodily harm to anyone in the vicinity.

Greg managed to maneuver over to the upside-down raft, had one of his passengers grab onto the bow line, and was pulling both rafts into an eddy. I looked upstream to see Dean and Wally make it safely through Crystal, and begin rowing towards the same eddy as Greg.

Finally we were all tied up to rocks on the shore, and Greg was organizing a boat turning party. Ropes were secured on the raft frame front and rear, and over the raft.

"Give us a hand here Charly," said Dean. I helped him climb on the exposed bottom of the raft and grabbed the two ropes. Everyone else formed two lines up on shore, each group holding one of the lines that were over the boat. On Greg's command Dean and I, standing on the inside tube closest to shore, pulled on the lines using our weight to push the inside tube down while the others pulled the ropes hand-over-hand up the shore. Slowly the heavy raft lifted up, reaching seventy-five degrees before Dean and I jumped off. As the raft reached the vertical, Dean shoved the lower tube away from shore and the raft completed the last quarter of its 180 degree spin with a resounding thump as it returned to its rightful position.

James jumped on board and started checking to see if there was any damage or equipment loss. "Looks like all that was lost was the extra coffee pot. Guess we were lucky this time. Sorry for the blunder."

"Don't worry about it, James." Greg interjected, "You know the saying, 'There are only two kinds of guides: those that have . . . and those that are gonna.' Welcome to the club. We're all glad it wasn't worse. We've still got the Gems to run before we get to camp. Let's get going."

The Gems are named after precious and semi-precious stones, Agate, Sapphire, Turquoise, Onyx, Ruby, and Serpentine. They are medium to medium-high rapids that would have seemed awesome before today. After Horn, Granite, Hermit and Crystal, they were just fun. It's odd how your perception can change so quickly. If we had run any of the Gems on the first couple of days, we would have been terrified.

We arrived at Bass Camp, at mile 108, late in the afternoon. We were all spent, but somehow the guides managed to put together another delicious meal. During dinner, Greg announced tomorrow would be a "more mellow" day, and we could all sleep in. There was a round of applause.

The walls of the Canyon seemed lower because the rim was farther away. Instead of the narrow slit we'd been used to, we had a much wider view of the sky. Another memorable image was etched in the photo album of my mind as dessert was served, accompanied by a fiery sunset. A fitting close to a red-hot river day.

Chapter Thirteen

Lessons

The sun crept over the rim and the warmth bathed my face. It was going to be hot. Greg had indeed allowed us to sleep in. No one else was stirring, but I was wide awake. I had noticed a trail last evening at dinner leading up to a ridge behind our camp. I thought it would provide a good viewing point and decided to take a hike. As an afterthought, I threw my journal into my backpack. The events of the past two days were so compelling, I wanted to remember every detail. I felt if I didn't write it down, much would be lost in the distant, unreachable synapses of my brain.

I filled my water bottle and headed out. As I emerged from camp, I startled a spotted skunk, in search of a late meal before her daily retreat from people and the sun. Her black and white tail stood straight up, reminding me of some wild hair styles I'd seen back in college. I laughed to myself and gave her a wide berth fearing her wrath if I ventured too close. A red-tailed hawk soared overhead, its laser vision searching the slopes for any movement that might mean breakfast.

As I walked, I thought about my first day in Arizona. I hadn't been attracted to the desert landscape. Coming from the midwest with all its greenery, the desert seemed devoid of most life. What life I had seen, cactus and shrubs, communicated the struggle all life had in a water deprived environment. After being in the desert twenty-four hours a day for seven days, I was growing to appreciate the tenacity of life, as well as its creativity. I hadn't thought of plants as having intelligence, but these plants had adapted to the climate by developing strategies to hold on to precious moisture. The creosote bush had a waxy, hairy surface, with a minimum number of pores to prevent water loss. Many of the animals, such as the skunk, were nocturnal, avoiding the dehydrating effect of the scorching desert sun. Throughout the day there seemed to be an ongoing and orderly procession of critters seeking to survive. Lizards took turns foraging for food, appearing at different hours. The first were the Tree and Side-blotch variety, then the long, comical Whiptails. Next came the Collard and Spiny lizards. Each seemed to have a scheduled feeding slot, and they punched in and out with their internal time clocks. And so it went with the rest of the wildlife. The birds and snakes were attuned to the schedule of the lizards and made their appearance in the ongoing dance of survival.

I'd noticed on the first day that as the sun rises in the sky the desert activity recedes to a standstill. The empty, motionless space of the desert. But being a part of the life on the river afforded me an opportunity to watch the cycles unfold. I had a chance to appreciate the connection of all things. I remembered Dean saying that if a species of plant were removed from the Canyon, it would impact everything else in the Canyon. He had used the example of the Coyote Willow, which was a favorite of the beaver. The building of Glen Canyon Dam eliminated the annual spring floods, and created a more stable high-water line. As a result tamarisk trees (also known as salt cedar), imported from the Middle East in the 19th century, had become established along this new line and reduced the space available for the willow. With less willow, the beaver had begun to disappear. Apparently they didn't like the taste of the tamarisk. The cycles of the beavers' natural predators, fox, coyote, and bobcat were also affected. Dean mentioned that the insect populations that had inhabited the willow were different than those preferring the tamarisk. Certain birds were partial to certain insects, and so man's intervention had once again altered Mother Nature.

My thoughts migrated to the indigenous peoples once living here. There is no evidence the original inhabitants navigated the river. Was it a source of wonder or a source of fear? Did they appreciate the beauty, or was it just another location to extract whatever could be found to sustain life? When they built the granary at Nankoweap, did they stop and marvel at the scenery, or was it as Sprit Dancer had said, just a location ensuring the safety of their food supply?

What about the earliest non-native visitors? From my pre-trip reading, I learned the earliest visitors thought it one more insurmountable barrier. A big inconvenience. The first recorded explorer had been Captain Garcia Lopez de Cardenas, an officer under the command of Francisco Vasquez de Coronado. He was well known for terrorizing and subjugating many of the natives of the Southwest and Mexico in his search for the legendary Seven Cities of Cibola.

Cardenas had sent three of his soldiers into the Canyon and they returned with a report that there was no way through. No record of non-native visitation or exploration was recorded for another 200 years.

I remembered George, my welcome hitchhiking companion crossing Nebraska. He had talked of the one-armed Civil War Major, John Wesley Powell and his first real exploration in 1869. From that time on through the 1940s, fewer than a hundred people had run the river. Actually until the eighties, the Canyon had been viewed as a place only for fools and adventurers. I almost laughed out loud when I imagined Powell's group of explorers rowing a wooden boat backward through some of the Canyon's major rapids for the first time.

I reached the ridge and looking down toward camp I could see some movement. Still, the Canyon peace was interrupted only by the faint sound of a small rapid downstream, and an occasional call from the Canyon Wren. I had become especially fond of this small bird whose strong set of vocal chords sent a playful descending trill through the Canyon. The sun had climbed higher in the sky, and I settled into a spot shaded by some large boulders.

As I drank from my water bottle, I flipped though my journal. My first entries were of the feelings I'd experienced on day one, when we'd moved into the current at Lees Ferry and later passed under the Navajo Bridge. Looking at the words I'd written, "welcome home, brother, welcome home," sent shivers down my spine and a smile to my face. It was true, I was feeling more at home every day.

I turned several pages. I had written about how unusual the Little Colorado had seemed after experiencing the BIG Colorado. The next few pages contained notes on Richard's challenging hike up to the granaries. I flipped to my encounter with Spirit Dancer at the Little "C" and her teaching on Effortless Energy. There was a description of the Great Unconformity, and my experience at Hance, where my perception of doom had changed so quickly to one of exhilaration. I was remembering my conversation with Marian about purpose and doing what you love when I heard the now familiar tinkling sound of Spirit Dancer's eagle necklace.

I turned my head to my left, where the sound seemed to be coming from, but didn't see her. I twisted to the right and finally all the way around, but she was nowhere in sight. My mind and ears must be playing tricks on me. I got up for a better view of camp. The only movements I could see were made by Greg and Marian walking on the beach. As I sat back down, the sun's position forced me to move a little to the left to remain in the shade. My attention was drawn to an eagle soaring directly in front of me. I watched for a couple of minutes and then looked back at my journal. The next entry was about Richard and the others hiking out and the Chance's arrival. I turned several more pages and studied what I'd written about James' flip in Crystal.

As I sat there looking at the snaking river reflecting the sun's rays, I suddenly heard Spirit Dancer say, "What does all this tell you about you, Charly?" She startled me and I felt as if I'd jumped a foot in the air.

"How do you do that? Where did you come from?" I blurted out, feeling my heart race for a moment.

"Sorry if I frightened you," she said calmly, and then paused. "It's not enough to record the events. Your task is to bring them back to you. What are the learnings from your experiences?"

Still annoyed by my reaction to her sudden presence, and now becoming annoyed at her question, I pushed the point. "Where did you come from? I didn't see you come up the path," I said.

She smiled and turned her head toward the river. As she moved, I noticed an eagle's feather clinging to her black hair. I looked out over the river in the direction where I'd seen the eagle soaring a few minutes before. I didn't see it.

"Charly," she said patiently. "remember there are two ways for you to gain insight through others. First, by being observant, and second by identifying the reflection in you. It's not people's actions that speak to you about you, it's how you perceive them."

I turned from looking out over the river and noticed a second feather a few feet behind her. Absentmindedly I said, "What?"

"What are the learnings, Charly? What do these experiences tell you about you? You have work to do." Her image was dissolving in the bright sunlight, and her voice was becoming fainter.

"Wait," I said. "I wanted to ask you about a dream I had. All I remember are the words 'conscious transition. Spirit Dancer!" I stared after her and then noticed the two feathers lying on the ground. I got up and retrieved them, feeling their texture. I placed them back on the ground, knowing it was illegal to have an eagle's feathers in my possession, and wanting the next person passing by to enjoy them. I sat back down, picking up the journal once more.

I drew a line down the middle of the page. On one side I wrote, "What are the learnings?" and on the other "What does this tell me about me?" I decided to record the learnings first, and then what they mean to me. Richard's difficulty in reaching the granaries was rewarded by his sense of accomplishment in achieving his objective, and the unexpected view he could not have imagined when he started the hike. What that means to me is how important it is to realize that many meaningful objectives will appear daunting at the beginning or halfway up. Keeping my eye on the goal and staying focused on my commitments will be rewarded by a sense of accomplishment and other payoffs that are often unknown immediately or unanticipated.

The learnings from the Wheel of Effortless Energy were many. First, success in any endeavor begins with the truth and requires trust. Second, in order to enjoy the journey, I have to slow down so I can "receive" the messages that are all around. Third, I have to be aware of balance, and in particular, what causes me to get out of balance. Otherwise, I won't be able to align with the Environmental Cues I receive. What this means for me is that I have to make a fresh start on how I am in the world.

Since I have been dishonest with myself most of my life, I have to learn how to be honest by telling the truth. Many of my decisions have been based on whether or not I would get approval from others. So they were, in effect, non-decisions, or choices I made to get others to accept and like me. Often those choices were not my preference. I had failed to develop the muscle which is necessary to tell the truth, to say, "Hell YES or NO" based on my values, needs and wants, not someone else's. This would not be easy.

Learning to be trusting and in the present would be a challenge, but I had some wonderful examples of that from the guides on this trip. In a conversation with Dean I learned that the only way to be consistently safe and make it through without flipping is to be present. If the mind is wandering, the consequences could be ugly. Marian told me she had to learn to be trusting. Once you shove off from shore, it's too late to worry about what might happen. Before running any major rapid, she would always say a prayer to the river gods, surround herself and the boats with white light, and thank the ancestors of the Canyon for providing safe passage. Then she would shove off and be focused only on making a good run. I was glad she told me that because it is something I can use when I'm facing my rapids back home and on the job.

The lesson from the Great Unconformity was to make almost anything in human time seem inconsequential. It takes up to a thousand years for enough sediment to form to create one inch of rock. That tells me two things. First, a Grand Canyon, or any work of enduring art, cannot be built overnight. Today, everything is in fifteen and thirty second sound bites and the most challenging situations are resolved in the course of a thirty minute television program or a two hour movie. We have come to expect doctors to cure us of our problems immediately with a pill. This quick-fix mentality pervades everything, including relationships, money, health, and spirituality. What this means for me is that I can't expect others to do "it" for me. I have to be willing to accept personal responsibility for my health, my success, my spirituality, my relationships. I need to be willing to do what it takes to create a work of art, one step at a time, no matter how long it takes.

The second thing I see is that my problems, while appearing important, are really of little significance seen in the context of a bigger picture. If I were to consider how important any of my problems were and who would remember them in just the period of time it takes to build one inch of sediment, I would see how inconsequential they really are. In a thousand years, none of my problems will be remembered, nor will I, in all likelihood. So what's the point of giving so much energy to my fears and worries? Should I pay attention to them? Of course. Should I do anything but use them as feedback, opportunities to learn and grow? Not if I want to enjoy my life. And I do.

Perhaps for the first time, I see how much control I have over how I feel and how I react. James' reaction to his flip was a good lesson in that for me. Many people would have been traumatized by being trapped under a boat, running out of air and heading for certain disaster. Instead, James said he came out of that experience with a positive affirmation for life. Instead of being frightened and not wanting to be a guide, he was excited because he felt like a survivor. He was sure he had some guardian angels looking out for him. And he said he felt he had more to do on the planet before he died.

To me this is a reminder that life is a perceptual experience and we choose the perception. So no matter what happens, I have the power to choose what I do about it and how I feel about it. Its not about fear, or anger, it's about what happens when they arise. It's about who determines my choices.

I could see how important knowing my purpose is, and I certainly wanted to have a job that I loved. But I didn't know either my purpose or what I loved. So I just noted that I needed to learn about both of these, and left it at that, saying I would make the time to determine my purpose before I left the Canyon, and would explore what I loved when I returned to the "real world". I still thought the real world was "out there," but further prodding from the real "real world" would enlighten me before I finished this trip.

I continued my journal entries. Hance. What about Hance? It was about perception. In a very short time, I had gone from certain death to exhilaration. What had changed? Well, first, I received some information I didn't have, notably, how to make it through the rapid safely. Since I didn't know how to read the river, I couldn't see it. James helped me see there was a way through. That at least reduced the anxiety. The second learning was how much different things felt when I was given an opportunity to get involved. Now I have no illusion that I had anything to do with getting us through Hance safely. That was all James' doing. But the fact that he asked me to help, so I wasn't just a spectator hoping for a safe outcome, made a world of difference.

What you focus on expands. It was much better to focus on my "job" of helping him keep track of the rapids. If I were the spectator, I would be afraid of something bad happening. I would be in the future, not the present. And I certainly wouldn't be trusting. Because I was focused on my "job," I was very present, and much more trusting. Somehow I knew things would be all right. So that was a good example of the Wheel of Effortless Energy.

I then remembered Richard and the group hiking out, as well as the Chances who hiked in. Something felt incomplete about that whole exchange, but I couldn't identify it. Then the word "transitions" entered my mind. There had been no "conscious ending," and there was as yet no "conscious new beginning."

I had done a lot of work with this concept as a consultant before my current job. It was based on the work of William Bridges, who created a model for managing transitions brought about by change. Bridges said there are three stages to any transition: endings, neutral zone, and new beginnings. In order for the new beginnings to be effective, you have to go through the first two stages. Richard and four others had hiked out. While there was a small ceremony the night before, there hadn't been any conscious ending. To be conscious, there should have been an opportunity for everyone to contribute. That contribution could be anything perceived as important, from talking about the loss, to acknowledging what the people leaving had given us, to an invitation to stay in touch.

When someone leaves a group, the dynamics change. Those who hiked out had shared some meaningful times with us, and now they are gone. Any unexpressed sense of loss can become a barrier to welcoming anyone new into the group. It's like having a pink elephant in the room that no one acknowledges, blocking the formation of a fully functioning group.

When you enter a group after they have shared meaningful times, you are also out of the loop. Anything the people who remain can do to bring the newcomers into the group, like sharing any experiences during the first five days, will make everyone's transition easier. We hadn't worked to bring the Chances into the group, and even though they are fine people and we get along, there is still a distance between us that can only be bridged by a formal welcoming. This is true whether its on a river trip, or at the office, or in the family. I made a note to share this with Greg.

Far below I heard the first conch shell offering up the nectar of the Gods to the caffeine dependent. I knew it would take another fifteen or twenty minutes before the breakfast call, and I had one more event to enter in my journal: the flip at Crystal.

Two things struck me about Crystal. The first was how dramatically this place had been altered by a naturally occurring event, namely a flash flood. It falls in the realm of the natural world and what it is teaching us—if we're willing to pay attention and learn. In this case, it has to do with judgments like good or bad. Some people would say it was a great event because it created this incredible, challenging rapid for us to run. They would be in the minority. Others, perhaps most, would say the flood was a bad thing because it created a dangerous spot on the river where there used to be none. Of course, that would be looking at it in human terms, a time span of around seventy or so years. How many times had that spot been altered in its six to fifty million year existence? Chances are it had been far more dangerous more than once.

Either point of view has inherent limitations. In truth, what happens in the natural world is neither good nor bad. There are consequences, to be sure. But change is the natural order of things, and humans are the only living creatures that resist it. I was learning to differentiate on this trip between what is natural and what has become normal in our lives. Change is natural. Resisting it is normal. Having multiple viewing points is natural. Having only one view point has become normal. We have become comfortable with black and white, right and wrong distinctions. It's a convenient way to maintain control through fear. It's a very poor way to resolve the problems that plague us.

Life is a perceptual experience. James could have been traumatized by his flip. He could have been seriously injured, or worse, had he not escaped from his submerged air chamber. After he flipped, he found himself under his raft in need of air. All he had time to do was find an air pocket in the footwell of his overturned raft. After he took that first breath and composed himself, he became fascinated with his situation.

As he described it to me, his first thought was about his breath. He could hear it echoing in the air chamber, and it reminded him that it was one of many things about his body he took for granted. Like what a true miracle the body is. He said his second thought was, 'just yesterday I washed my hair in this forty-eight degree water and frosted my brains. Now here I am, totally submerged in it, and not in the least aware of its temperature."

It was the body's survival mechanism that rechanneled the flow of blood from the surface to the internal organs to provide a better chance for survival. In emergencies, the brain automatically marshals its forces and shuts down the flow of blood to the extremities, including the skin, so that more blood can be sent to the organs, like the brain and heart, that are essential for survival.

I had asked James whether he was now afraid of the river. His response was heartening. He said, "I certainly have more respect for its power. If anything, I feel more comfortable because of the flip."

I was stunned by that reply, "How so?" I asked. "You could have been killed out there. What was it about the experience that could possibly make you more comfortable?"

"Well, I flipped in the most dangerous rapid in the Canyon for a flip. And I ended up in the worst possible place, under my raft. After all was said and done, and I was sitting on my cooler thawing out, I realized I was a survivor. I still had things to accomplish on the planet, and there was something protecting me, keeping me from harm. It was a great feeling, one that makes me smile as I speak about it. I'm sure I'll be nervous the next time I run Crystal, but I'm looking forward to a rematch. And this time, instead of fighting the river, I'll go with it."

I thought about what he had said, and concluded that I could be more grateful for all my body does for me. I would use his flip to remind me that when I go through a tough situation I'll probably survive, and I can use the experience to stretch and grow. It's never the experience that is important. It's how I choose to respond to it, and what I choose to do as a result of it.

I closed my journal and took a deep breath. There had been so much going on during the last two days, I hadn't realized there were so many lessons. I was sure there were more, and I had no doubt Spirit Dancer would inform me if that was the case.

I stood up and reached for the sky to stretch out the kinks that had developed from my slouching against the rock. I glanced down. The two eagle feathers were still lying on the ground. At that moment, I heard the breakfast conch blow. I marveled at the way its note expanded to fill the entire Canyon, echoing off the walls as it traveled upstream and back into the Inner Gorge. The thought struck me that the conch at one time enjoyed a life on the bottom of the ocean. It seemed apropos that it would now interject its vibration into the gorge which many times had been covered by vast seas.

I headed down to breakfast. I was very excited and felt alive. I had the distinct feeling that a lifetime had passed, although I'd only ascended to the ridge top a couple hours earlier. I had walked around the wheel and found a viewing point that was more consistent with who I am. I had demonstrated to myself how much I could learn about me and the world around me, if I could just remain awake, as Spirit Dancer had said. I looked around feeling her presence again. I couldn't see her, but felt her smiling from a place just behind my heart.

Chapter Fourteen

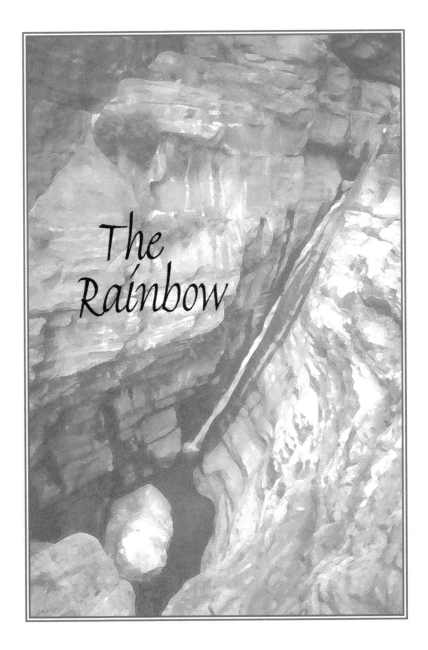

The
Rainbow

As I approached camp, I was struck by an unusual quiet. Normally breakfast is punctuated with a buzz of activity and conversation. Not this morning.

"Boy, you're a lively bunch," I chided. Several people nodded and mumbled something with their mouths full. They had expended so much energy the day before, they seemed only interested in replenishing their depleted bodies. Pancakes and sausage took precedence over conversation.

After filling my plate with "sinkers," the guide's name for the dense oat pancakes, I went over and sat with Greg on the front tube of his boat. I described to him my thoughts on closure for those who had left us, and the value of consciously bringing the Chances in to our river family. "A ceremony, maybe," I threw in. For several minutes he was silent, and I was starting to feel nervous. Had I stepped on his toes? Was I out of line?

He tipped the cowboy hat back, looked up and a slow smile came to his lips. "We'll have to do something about that," he said.

Greg wasn't one for a lot of words. I was relieved that he had seen value in what I'd suggested, pleased he would do something with it, and curious as to what that might be. He went back to eating and I moved over to talk with Jane.

After breakfast, we went through our usual clean-up procedures. The guides were more casual about rigging today as compared to the last two days. Obviously there would be less 'big water.'

I hurriedly threw my stuff in a bag, and was carrying it to James' boat when I saw Greg motioning for everyone to form a group.

"For those who want to hike, you'll have two opportunities today, Elves Chasm and Deer Creek." His slow manner of talking made Deer have too many 'eeerr's in it.

As I listened to his description of Elves Chasm, I pictured a magical kingdom of oddly shaped rocks and brilliantly colored vegetation. He informed us that we would see a 200 foot waterfall at Deer Creek. A short hike would take us up to what he called the patio. My excitement from my earlier revelations still had my adrenaline pumping and I was ready to go. I started to head to the rafts, and then I realized Greg wasn't done.

"Yesterday was a very intense time for all of us, but maybe most intense for the Chances," said Greg. Our attention turned to the new group of four people.

"We've experienced a lot together, most of it before the Chances joined us. Before we head downstream this morning, I would like to bring them up to speed. Give them a chance to catch up, so to speak. I thought it would be nice for each of you to introduce yourselves, say where you're from, and what's been one event or experience that has stood out for you on the upper part of our trip. We don't need long stories. I just want them to get a feel for our first six days. During the day today, you can talk to them individually and share in more depth. Who would like to start?"

Frank, with his usual aggressive behavior, was the first to speak. I noticed, and appreciated that he was wearing a shirt even though it was going to be a hot day.

The Chances seemed to hang on everyone's words, especially young Nathan. I watched his eyes, alive with wonder. When it was my turn, I shared my embarrassing moment in Thirty-six Mile rapid and what it taught me about taking the river for granted. Nathan's eyes were as big as saucers as I ended.

When we finished, the Chances were clearly feeling more a part of the group, and I was impressed with how easy it had been to accomplish. It was also interesting to hear how unique each person's experiences were. We had all been through the same events, but everyone was taking something different home with them. Thoughts and feelings emerged that hadn't during normal conversations. It seemed others had been reflecting as I had. I gave Greg a big smile, and got a smile and small nod in return.

I looked down, and there was Nathan at my side. "Hey, Charly, I want to go on your boat today."

"If it's okay with your parents," I said, looking over at Jack who smiled and nodded his approval.

Walking toward the boats, I noticed a puzzled look on Nathan's face. Very seriously, he asked, "How old do you think I'd have to be before the guides would let me row one of the boats?"

"Well, certainly not this year," his mom replied. "At least not anywhere close to a rapid."

"If you get to row, I'm jumping in the water and swimming," exclaimed Jessie with her hands on her hips. Nathan looked insulted.

Jack, Nathan, Jessie and I hopped on Dean's boat. Fran had been talking with Marian. She waved to us and climbed onto her boat. After two days of whitewater intensity, it felt good just to kick back and enjoy the scenery. We had emerged from the inner gorge yesterday after completing the Gems, and were once again in the Cambrian rock formation, the Tapeats sandstone. The last time we'd seen this sandstone at river level was in the vicinity of the Little Colorado, sixty miles behind us up stream.

Dean offered to let me row and after a moment of hesitation, I decided to give it another try. By now I had no illusion as to who or what was in control. It certainly wasn't me. I concentrated on keeping the boat in the current, hitting the waves straight, and staying out of the eddies.

When I'd started this trip, I was under the impression that water only went with gravity, straight downstream. I was realizing that in the Canyon, the current is fairly narrow in many places, and it doesn't go straight downstream. Instead, it snakes, undulating within the river channel, creating swirls and boils of water that rise from the obstructions on the river bottom, sounding like a retreating ocean wave at the shoreline as it fights its way through the next advancing wave. On either side of the snake-like current are often eddies, the bodies of surface water that are moving upstream against the natural flow of the current. Rapids are formed when debris gets pushed into the river. This narrows the river channel, but the same volume of water had to go somewhere, so the current must speed up. As soon as the river widens, it slows, spreads out, and becomes lazy again. I realized, as with all things in nature, the river is always seeking balance.

Keeping Spirit Dancer's lesson of Effortless Energy in mind, I tried to stay out of the eddies. I had seen how much distance was lost when boats drifted into them. Dean showed me how to "feel" the change in current speed as I was getting close to an eddy and how to avoid it.

He explained, "When 51% of the boat is in the eddy, it will pull all of the boat in.." He made circular motions with his arms. "So your job is to make sure 51% of the boat stays in the downstream current. When you get closer to an eddy, say on the left side, your left oar will move easier through the water because that current will be moving slower than the main current. Your tendency will be to push on both oars, but in so doing, your right oar will be meeting more resistance and will push the boat to the left, guaranteeing your entry into the eddy."

I nodded and kept up a smooth pace.

Nathan turned from his seat up front and said, "Yeah, you're really doing great, Charly. Need any help?" From behind me, Jessie chimed in as well about the great part, but reiterated that if anyone let her brother row, she was swimming. It was obvious I had a couple of new friends.

Dean half laughed and continued, "What you have to do will not make sense at first. You have to push harder on the left oar to steer the boat away from the eddy and back towards the current. One little trick I use is to keep your right oar in the water while using your left oar. It keeps you moving downstream as you correct the position of the boat." His love for the river was evident, as it had been during our pre-trip spaghetti dinner lectures.

He shaded his eyes and studied the river. "Okay, there's one coming up. You can try it."

After a few false starts, I got the hang of it, and then it became a challenge, my competitive nature rising. I thanked Dean for his suggestions and felt a deep sense of satisfaction as I became more comfortable. But, I made a deliberate effort not to become cocky. As I pulled on the oars and felt the sun on my face, again the thought of actually becoming a river guide edged into my consciousness. A cold water slap in the face brought my attention back to the task at hand.

We entered a section of the river where the granite rose out of the earth, alternately lifting the Tapeats sandstone up and then lowering it back down, returning it to its underground hideaway. Dean pointed out one place where the sandstone was actually folded almost ninety degrees.

"Wow!" said Nathan. "Rock that was bent, but not broken."

"Right Nathan," said Dean. "It occurred very, very slowly over many millennia. It's called the Monument Fold."

"What's millennia?" asked Nathan.

"A veeerrrrry long time, Nathan," said Jack. Everyone laughed.

I thought it looked like a terra cotta design created by some giant sculptor. As I studied it, I was reminded of the persistence, patience, and power of nature. Water, for instance, resists nothing. It always backs up when finding some obstacle, and seeks the path of least resistance. Eventually it finds a way around, under or over, and in time removes the obstacle. I remembered a Burdock plant I'd seen in an asphalt parking lot back in Michigan. Man had attempted to impose his will upon the natural world, but had failed. As seemingly fragile as it was, through it's persistent, microscopic movement, the Burdock found its way into the light by simply pushing through the asphalt.

Great, enduring things are created slowly, over time. The same is true about the accomplishments of humans, only in more "human" terms. I thought about the old adage, "Life begins at forty," in recognition that we have persisted in gaining wisdom, knowledge, and skills. The impatience of my normal life, as well as that of most others, expressed in our, "get-rich-quick-by-winning-the-lottery," and "give-me-a-pill-and-make-me-better-doc" approaches to life provide little opportunity to tap into the richness that life really offers.

I realized my mind had been wandering and was shaken off my philosophical musings by Dean requesting the oars. "We have to pull over here, and the current is a little tricky. Better let me handle this."

I wasn't about to argue, although I did feel a little twinge of disappointment. I was definitely hooked on being behind the oars, and wanted to learn as much as possible. Several times during the morning, I'd found myself imagining a future trip with me at the oars of my own boat. It seemed farfetched and unrealistic, but the desire was getting more air time in my mind.

The tricky pull over turned out to be our arrival at Elves Chasm. The hike began with a quarter mile walk, slightly uphill along a trail of granite and travertine, with several boulder-sized rocks to scramble over. Nathan and Jessie appeared by my side within a few steps after departure. I decided to show off some of my pre-trip knowledge. I explained to the kids that travertine is a form of limestone carried in solution in water. "It builds on itself much like coral combines to create reefs. When untouched by humans, it weathers into dark rock with multitudes of sharp edges that can rip clothes and skin. But, when worn down by foot traffic, as on this trail, it becomes like polished white limestone, beautiful and very slippery."

As I said slippery, Nathan began to clown and act like he was falling. Jessie admonished him for being silly.

Jack joined us, asking "Hey kids, what does this canyon remind you of?"

Jessie thought a minute, then said, "It reminds me of the Hobbit story that you read to us Dad."

"I was thinking the same thing," I said. Jessie beamed.

It was a fairy land of rocks and water, yellow columbine, cardinal monkey flower, and maiden hair fern. At one point we had to bridge a two-foot gap between two large boulders. The kids leaped across without hesitation, but it was interesting that several of the adults needed reassurance and a helping hand, which the guides were happy to offer.

We edged around a house-sized boulder, eased across another short gap, stepped gingerly on a polished, travertine-covered boulder, and then stepped up onto a short sandstone ledge. As we came around a corner, we were greeted by a narrow waterfall plunging delicately into a shimmering pool bracketed by steep sandstone walls. In front of the pool was a cluster of cardinal monkey flower creating a perfect foreground for the photograph I was about to take.

"We'll be here for about an hour," Greg announced. "You can swim behind the waterfall, climb above it and jump into the pool if you want. Wally will show you how."

Wally had been bringing up the rear of the hiking party and I could tell he was glad to expend some pent-up energy. He stripped off his shirt, waded in, and began swimming towards the falls. Nathan immediately headed after him, but was stopped by his mom.

"Not so fast there, young man," Fran said, grabbing her son by the arm and pulling him back.

We all watched as Wally disappeared into the shadows behind the walls. Within a minute he appeared above the waterfall, lowered himself to the lip near the spout and waved. Several others already had cameras poised, and he jumped into the pool to clicking cameras and shouts of glee. Today, Nathan and Jessie were not the only children in the group. Wally's playfulness and the fairy-tale aura of this place helped bring out the child in many of us. Before long several had ventured into the darkness behind the falls and taken their own plunge accompanied by shouts of encouragement from the rest. I noticed Frank, seeming a little more mellow after eight days. He took the plunge, sans shirt of course.

After persistent pleading from Nathan and Jessie, Fran looked at Jack and me.

"Will you two take them?" she asked in a worried tone.

"Let's go kids," Jack said, as anxious as the children. Fran had relented, but still looked a little nervous.

Nathan didn't give her a second to change her mind. "Come on, Charly," he said grabbing my hand. Jessie took her Dad's and we headed toward the falls.

As the kids held their noses and jumped, their shouts of delight added to everyone's joy. We climbed up numerous times, and no one was ready when Greg gave us a five minute warning. Reluctantly we climbed out of the water and gathered our gear. A stream of people began heading back to the boats. I stayed behind a couple more minutes to take a few more photographs. I was stuffing my camera in my day pack when I took one last look at the water feeding into the falls. It was coming from a source higher in the side canyon which Greg had said included several more layers. The water appeared as a small vertical stream and split into two streams like long, flowing white hair draped around a face. As I looked at the water, I could actually see the shape of a face with two narrow eyes, a long nose, and a mouth shaped in a wry smile. It must be the elf in Elves Chasm, I thought. It struck me that if I stuck around long enough, he might appear and talk to me as Spirit Dancer did. It must be a wise elf, having seen so much over the years. I gave him a parting salute, and hurried to catch up with the group.

We lunched in the shade of a small side canyon called Blacktail. Marian said it was the closest thing in the Canyon to a slot canyon, with sandstone walls almost touching in spots. It was a quick stop, and then we were on the river again, heading for Deer Creek.

Dean made effortless runs through rapids with names like Fossil, Spectre, Bedrock and another big rapid called Dubendorff. He then handed me the oars. I was becoming more comfortable on them, feeling my way downstream, so for a change I could take the time to notice the scenery. Dean used his free time for a geology lesson. The water followed a rock layer called basalt, lava walls that lay underneath Bass limestone. At the point where the lava and the limestone contacted was a narrow band of asbestos, and a semi-precious milky green stone called serpentine.

The river was a little wider here. Breaks in the canyon walls provided glimpses of both the north and south rims, many miles away in the distance and four to six thousand feet above us. Once again I realized, that being on the river gave us a limited picture of the vastness of the Canyon. Only when you catch a view of the rim do you get a vague idea of how massive it really is.

Then all of a sudden the walls pushed in, almost giving me a feeling of claustrophobia. I had felt a little better rowing with more space on both sides. Dean said it was the narrowest spot in the channel, less than seventy-six feet from one side to the other.

He continued to explain, "Several million years ago an earthquake caused a massive rock slide that dammed up the river channel. Undaunted, the river merely backed up and looked for a new route."

I smiled as I remembered my thoughts from earlier that morning about water seeking the path of least resistance. This was apparently another example.

"It decided to carve a new channel through the very hard granite just below and south of the old channel," he pointed as he talked.

We were closed in by granite cliffs. The calm current attested to the depth of the river at this point. We floated in silence, with everyone mesmerized by the beauty. Even the kids were speechless.

In ten minutes we were pulling up to a muddy beach on the right side of the river. The sound of massive water plunging from a great height greeted us, but it wasn't until the boats were tied up and we crossed a small creek that we saw the source of all the noise. Less than a hundred yards from the river was an impressive 200 foot waterfall shooting out from between the Tapeats sandstone that towered over us.

Marian initiated a hike and nearly everyone followed her up a steep trail carved out of the granite by natural forces, reinforced by thousands of footsteps. As they left, I overheard Wally describing the waterfall's origin to the group.

His voice rose so that everyone could hear. "This water began its journey in the ocean, then rose high into the atmosphere as evaporated water, moved east powered by prevailing winds, and dropped onto the North Rim as either rain or snow. It then traveled through the underlying rock layers, drawn by gravity, until it met the impermeable Muav limestone layer. There it backed up into a huge underground lake, and through its inexorable drive to return to the ocean, ate its way out through the limestone bed containing it, becoming the source for Deer Creek. By the time it reached its apex at the top of the falls, it had completed more than half its journey through the hydrological cycle, one of the many miracles in the natural world where all things are connected."

Feeling very mellow, I had decided to hang out near the waterfall. I watched everyone depart and then leisurely walked up the small stream created by the waterfall and came to the edge of the pool created by the falls. I had a sudden urge to explore. The sun was hot on my back, and I waded in, the cool water surrounding my calves. The energy generated by the water falling two hundred feet produced a strong wind as I got closer to the cascading water. The air was saturated with moisture, a heavy mist. Now in over my head, I began swimming towards the base of the falls. The closer I got, the stronger the wind became. I'm a strong swimmer, but the force of the wind was even stronger. I dove underwater to escape. Not knowing exactly where I was, I surfaced just in front of the fall's plunge into the river. The peaceful water of the pool had suddenly become angry, and pushed me into a swirling, dark mass of chaos. When I surfaced again, I was twenty-five feet back, and it was very clear who had more power.

I was determined to see what was behind the falls, so I tried again. This time, when the force started to push me back, I took a deep breath, submerged and swam ahead. My parents had always said I was a fish out of water, and I was excited by this new adventure. I felt a mixture of curiosity and fear as I entered the turmoil of the plummeting falls overhead. What would I find behind the falls?

Thump! It was a rock wall. I rose to the surface and was at first confused and a little scared. There was very little space behind the falls, and with the spray hitting me in the face, I had a hard time getting a breath. The deafening roar and rush of energy from the constant two-hundred foot free falling water was incredible. I gulped another breath and pushed off the wall, swimming back under the falls.

Surfacing, I relaxed and treaded water. Looking up, I watched the leaping water shoot out from its rocky crest, and then, caught in the inevitable grasp of gravity, plunge to the pool in front of me. With a smile of appreciation, I turned and swam back to the middle of the pool, found the bottom with my feet and stood up. Then I saw what at first seemed like an impossible phenomenon. I was transfixed. Surrounding me was a rainbow, a 360 degree rainbow! I had never seen anything like it. A brilliant ring of red, orange, yellow, green, blue, indigo and violet. My heart rejoiced. My face was bathed with moisture. I touched my skin. Was it the drops from the heavy mist? It was warm, like tears. Tears of joy?

Such a simple, yet profound gift offered by nature. Rainbows have always awakened a child-like sense of wonder in me. I'm touched by their magical radiance. They seem to travel through my eyes directly into my heart, bringing a feeling that all is well with the world. Time ceased to move as I stood in that magical circle. I felt this rainbow was a sign that my morning revelations could truly begin to change my life.

I remembered Wally 's technical description of the source of the water, but erased the thoughts from my mind as I wiped the droplets from my cheeks. Here it was, dancing in front of me, merging with the sun's rays to create emotions that reached deep into my heart and soul. I felt so alive. Yes, it was my sign. It was clear how little I needed to be happy and feel fulfilled. There was no doubt I wanted more of this life. In that moment I made my choice and my commitment. Whatever it would take, I was coming back. I didn't know how or when, but I would do what I could to return to this incredible natural wonder. Rainbows were truly miracles.

The sound of cheerful voices announced the return of the hikers, who plunged into the pool to cool off. Eagerly I introduced everyone to the miracle of the wrap-around rainbow. Finally we returned to the rafts to complete our day's journey.

We floated downstream less than a mile and pulled over at a camp site the guides called Pancho's Kitchen. On the upstream side of the camp was an overhang that would provide protection in the event of rain, which was unlikely. Still basking in the wonder of my encircling rainbow, I ate dinner, found a campsite out in the open, and fell asleep to the gentle song of the river.

Chapter Fifteen

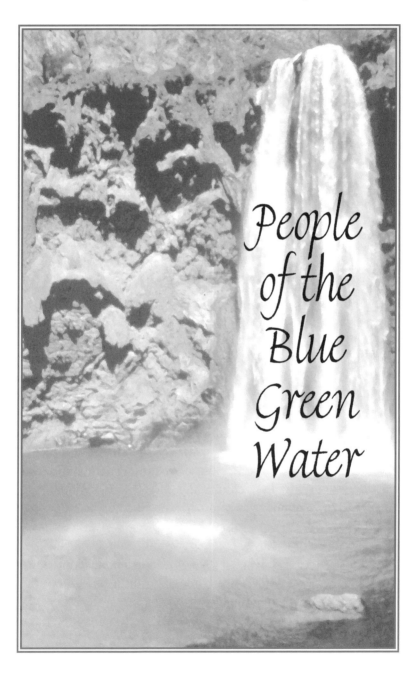

People
of the
Blue
Green
Water

The now familiar song of the conch mixed with the aroma of coffee introduced me to another day. As I lay in my bag I remembered the rainbow at Deer Creek two days ago, and my decision to return to the Canyon. Yesterday we'd floated a very beautiful section of the river the guides called the Muav gorge. The name came from the blue-gray Muav limestone which rose straight out of the river. The day had been very mellow with one exception, a rapid called Upset. I had been on Wally's boat, and he allowed me to row for quite awhile. I navigated through a number of the smaller rapids, and felt quite good about my performance. I learned a number of new things from him. Each guide has his own technique, but they all were very skilled in reading the river, seeing where they needed to go, and what they needed to avoid.

As I rowed, Wally talked about college in Arizona. He'd spent two summers in Utah collecting and counting aphids and separating them into small, medium, and large. The thought had occurred to me that biologists must be very patient people. The objects of their curiosity were often microscopic. No one on his boat could relate to that kind of tedious effort, but Wally acted like he enjoyed the experience. The rest of the morning he regaled us with hilarious stories. We laughed the hardest during a tale where he described having to separate the tiny insects by sex. I'd heard of gallows humor before, but this was the first time I'd been exposed, no pun intended, to biologist's humor.

We had camped in a very quiet part of the Canyon at a place known as Ledges. This had been the first camp where sand had been notable by its absence. The ledges were just that, platforms of Muav limestone ascending at varying heights from the river. It had been like a stone habitat, a cluster of open air condominiums. I had named my site the penthouse, because it was high above the river affording me a great overview of the boats and the kitchen. Most important, it afforded easy access to the bathroom.

The location of the bathrooms, or "unit" as the guides called it, was very important—usually close to the river, offering privacy to the user, as well as a spectacular natural mural. At the beginning of the trip, a lot of the passengers felt awkward about using the "facilities" in the open air. But, by now all seemed accustomed to the procedure, and didn't seem to show any discomfort. The least favorable comment I heard came from one of the women, who said "It's just something you get used to."

Before we wandered off to bed, Greg announced that we'd be spending tomorrow in a paradise called Havasu. He explained that the guides called this side canyon the "Garden of Eden." Eleven miles up the drainage was the Supai village, inhabited by some 300 Havasupai Indians. During the float, Wally told us some of their history. Havasupai means people of the blue-green water, referring to the color of the creek which runs through the reservation and spills into the Colorado. When I heard that, I immediately remembered my time at the Little Colorado which had been so visually stunning. I wondered how Havasu would compare.

Wally also told us that the Supai people historically occupied a much larger area than they currently inhabit. Beginning in the 1870's, they began a legal fight to take back the land they felt rightfully theirs. After nearly one hundred years, President Lyndon Johnson, in a last second decision, granted them a small portion of their ancestral lands. This land is outside the boundaries of Grand Canyon National Park, and today they are the only indigenous people living below the rim.

After dinner we made lunch for the next day. We were going to brown bag it because we would be in Havasu most of the day. I made two sandwiches, one with turkey, and of course, one with the traditional peanut butter and jelly. I also packed some cookies and nuts and an orange.

I'd been lying in my bag too long and now had to hurry. Greg was trying to get everyone to hustle so we could break camp. It seemed ironic because even as he talked of hustling, he did so in his slow cowboy drawl! With a big sweep of his hat toward the boats and a large grin on his face, I heard him say, "Let's move it campers."

We were floating by 7:30, and arrived at Havasu before 9:00. There was some initial excitement as the guides did a bit of boat wrangling, their term for getting all the boats into what they called the Hava-zoo parking lot. Apparently, every rafting company floating the river stops at Havasu. It was the closest thing we'd seen to "rush-hour traffic."

"On some days," Marian said, "there could be six or seven different companies and over a hundred people having a 'modified wilderness experience.'" She said "wilderness experience" with a smirk. Now I saw the importance of camping close by and Greg's insistence on rushing. It had paid off. We were the first to arrive.

As we secured the boats and unloaded what we needed, Marian went on, "Many of the motor companies only go up about a quarter mile and play in a pool we lovingly call 'the motor pool.' You have your choice, of course, and the motor pool is a beautiful pool, but if you want to avoid the teaming throngs, there's a great waterfall about three and a half miles up stream. It's called Beaver Falls. Dean and I will be leading the group to Beaver."

Dean chimed in with, "A third choice is to find a nice secluded shady spot and do whatever you want."

Marian nodded. "Something for everyone."

I was torn. I wanted to do it all. Go to Beaver, meander, do some writing.

Then Dean said, "Oh yeah, there's a subterranean cave underneath the falls that's really great."

My mind was made up. I would go to Beaver. If we got there fast enough, I could also take some time to journal. We started as a group, climbing the Muav stair steps that were now a familiar and convenient avenue to our destinations. We gained about fifty feet of elevation and looked down on our boats, tied in the Hava-zoo parking lot.

Our first view of the side canyon was indeed impressive. The translucent blue-green creek, a stunning contrast to the pewter hued limestone, descended through many pools that collected above mini-dams formed by boulders encased in travertine. Each of the dams created a small cascade of white water, which contrasted sharply with the beautiful color of the water. Next to the trail was a tall cactus which Dean said was called Ocotillo (pronounced oco-tee-yo). It had many straight, thorn-covered branches that rose vertically from a central location to a height of around twelve feet. Hundreds of small green leaves decorated each thorny spike, and they were topped with a beautiful red-orange blossom like a brilliant flame atop a candle.

We crossed the creek at the first of what would be many more crossings. The water was comfortably cool, and invited us to stop and swim, which we did on more than one occasion during the day. Continuing on, we could hear the creek, but couldn't see it. The vegetation was so lush it obscured the waters from our sight. If we hadn't just crossed it, we might have wondered what was causing the sound of rushing water.

In short order we arrived at the motor pool. It was very inviting, but I was determined to make it to Beaver and miss the masses. Dean told those who weren't going on to be back at the boats by 3:00 PM. The rest of us moved briskly on. After climbing through a tunnel carved into the travertine by some ancient flow of water, the forced march began. I sensed that Dean was about to put it in high gear, and I was right. With all the hiking we'd done over the years, his sustained pace still amazed me. He was only a couple of inches taller than me, but sometimes I was convinced his legs were a foot longer. I was determined to keep up.

This was one of the most beautiful places I had ever been in. In addition to the lush vegetation by the creek, which we could still hear but rarely saw, we hiked through dense forests of catclaw acacia trees, felt the soft touch of desert grasses brushing against our legs, and rushed through thick groves of wild grape leaves. Grapes in the desert? Another wonder in a place filled with delightful surprises. I paused to look around and had to jog to catch up. I found myself second guessing my decision to go to Beaver. The pace was so fast I had to concentrate on where I was stepping and didn't have time to enjoy what I was seeing.

After forty-five brisk minutes, we crossed the creek again and Dean announced, "This is our halfway point. Take a break, drink some water, cool off in the creek. But don't drink the water. It flows through the village and they have livestock up there. You never know what you'll catch."

He didn't have to tell me twice. I thought about my anti-climactic fall into the Little Colorado just as Marian was saying not to drink the water there. I still wasn't sure whether I'd swallowed any of the Little Colorado, but I hadn't gotten sick. As I jumped in to cool off, I knew my mouth was closed. I had no desire to catch something a cow would give me.

As I climbed out, some people had already dug out their sandwiches. It was just after ten in the morning, but our hurried pace had made us ravenous.

"Only five more crossings, and we'll be there," Marian volunteered and Jane groaned. "Actually we've done the hardest part. From here on it will go quickly."

She was right. Our pace didn't slow, but the peanut butter and jelly raised our blood sugar, giving us energy, and the swim had cooled us off. We adapted to Dean's strides.

I paid more attention to the scenery. The canyon walls rose high above us, blocking much of the sun, providing blessed shade. As we walked lizards scurried, playing a game of chance. They seemed to dare us to catch them as they raced in front of us and then disappeared into the dense foliage. More than once, the sound of rustling leaves off to the side startled me, conjuring up images of rattlesnakes on the attack. But, it was only the little guys.

We made our last crossing and climbed up a tenuous staircase carved into the Muav. Unlike many other trails in the Canyon, which were created by animals or ancient peoples, Dean told us this trail had been carved by Park Service trail maintenance crews. We walked along a narrow ledge high above the creek, and climbed a trail on a different kind of rock that looked and felt ancient.

I'd been looking at some plants and hadn't noticed the rock below my feet until I heard Jane say, "What are we walking on, Dean? This looks like the same rock we saw in Elves Chasm."

Dean nodded with a pleased look on his face. "You're right Jane. It's travertine. At one time there was a lot of water flowing through this part of the canyon. The travertine was carried in solution and built on itself just as you saw in the creek as we crossed it. I would have loved to have seen what it was like when the water was this high."

"Amazing. We must be at least ninety feet above Havasu creek," I said. "There must have been a huge amount of water here for a very long period of time."

"Must have," replied Dean.

Just then we came to the top of the trail and our attention was riveted on a spectacular view. It elicited a chorus of involuntary oohs and aahs, and then everyone just stared. About one hundred-fifty feet below was a pool of the deepest blue water I'd ever seen. To the left were several small cascades plunging into more striking pools, and about a quarter mile up the creek was our destination, Beaver Falls. From where we stood, it appeared to be a thirty-five foot cascade, disappearing into a jungle of ash and cottonwood trees.

Jane broke the silence. "Are you sure we are still in the desert? This looks like the Amazon or somewhere else in the tropics. It's so lush."

I was stunned, almost overwhelmed by the beauty. Calling this the Garden of Eden was no stretch of the imagination.

We followed Dean, almost hypnotized by the beauty all around us, down a trail to a spot about fifty feet above the first pool. Without warning, Dean slipped off his pack and dropped his sunglasses, and with a loud shout, jumped into the air. I was startled by his voice and the suddenness of his action. Looking over the edge, I watched him splash in the pool forty-five feet below.

When he surfaced, he had a huge smile on his face. He yelled back up, "All right, whose next?"

I really wanted to do it, but forty-five feet? It looked too scary. Jane grabbed my arm and dug her fingernails in. No one moved immediately. We looked at each other silently saying, "Okay, you go." But our feet were bolted to the rock. Dean began the climb back up. When he got to the top, we continued on towards Beaver.

I was already regretting my non-decision at the ledge. I followed closely behind Dean, engaged in some silent self recrimination. Maybe on the way back, I thought. We walked along the upper edge of the series of pools leading to Beaver, wove our way between spine filled beavertail cactus loaded with yellow and peach colored blossoms, and began our descent to the pools through a narrow, dusty cut in the rocks.

We followed Dean along a well trodden trail to the left of a large pool. We were back in the jungle which had caused Jane to comment earlier. Beaver was in the background sounding like a small jet on take-off. Nowhere is the power of water to create life more evident than right in the midst of an arid desert. The air was suddenly moist, reflecting the humidity of the rushing, cascading waters. With the extra humidity and shade provided by the trees surrounding the pool, the late morning desert temperature was lowered significantly. It felt wonderfully comfortable. Even Frank, who again managed to haul his corpulent frame up here, was awestruck.

"This is a paradise!" Frank proclaimed, dropping in the shade. He had been very quiet during the long, hot, demanding hike. "No wonder the Supai fought so long to get ownership of this land."

He appeared to be on a roll, and I wasn't in the mood for one of his discourses, so I decided to take a plunge. In spite of the cooler temperature in the shade, I was still overheated from the hike. In one continuous movement, my shirt came off over my head and I slipped off my shoes. Within seconds I was floating on my back. There wasn't a cloud in the sky, and I closed my eyes and completely relaxed. I shivered. The water was cooler than I thought, but very refreshing. The power generated by the cascade created a circulating eddy that carried me right up to the turbulent, frothy water. I rolled over and dove underwater, then let the current carry me away from the falls. When I surfaced I was some distance back. Feeling much better, I climbed out and returned to the shade where the others were devouring the remainder of their lunches, the part that hadn't been eaten on our first break.

I was digging in my pack when I suddenly heard Frank screaming. I turned to see him flailing his arms at an opportunistic raven. He had evidently left his lunch unattended while exploring the vegetation near the falls. Unnoticed, the iridescent black bird had actually opened Frank's pack, removed and opened a zip-locked plastic bag, and was flying away with his sandwich.

Marian and Jane, sitting side by side eating, had rolled over in the sand and were laughing hysterically. Frank was irate, and stood with hands on hips shaking his fist at the bird. There was nothing anyone could do. By now the thief was sharing the spoils with a friend. Between pecks, they were busy talking, undoubtedly complimenting each other for counting coup on another human victim.

As I looked at Frank's shirtless torso, the thought struck me that he certainly wasn't going to starve. At least not today. Marian was evidently feeling guilty for laughing so hard, and she offered Frank half of her second sandwich. Jane did the same. Dean offered an apple. Pouting, Frank sat down to eat the donated lunch.

"Don't leave your food unattended. You know better than that." Marian issued a warning with a snicker. Several others chuckled.

Undaunted by Frank's tirade, and evidently not completely satisfied, the vaudevillian pair gave us an aerobatics show, ending by swooping to the ground some distance from where we were sitting. We were fascinated with their humorous hop-like dance, as they began a surveillance to see if any other opportunities might arise. As we watched, Marian began telling us about a group who had hiked into North Canyon. The cook had left 24 frozen Halibut steaks behind thawing in five gallon buckets of water. Returning, she noticed a raven flying away from one of the buckets with a fish steak in its claws. Rushing to save the remainder of the steaks, she was horrified to find the buckets filled only with water. The ravens must have been having quite a feast.

As I ate my second sandwich, Dean came over and asked if I wanted to go into the Green Room, which was the subterranean cave directly underneath Beaver. I put the rest of my sandwich back in its bag, stuffed it in my backpack and placed a rock on top to thwart the wily ravens. The sandwich might be smashed, but at least it would still be there.

Dean jumped in and let the current take him to the edge of the frothy waters. I followed.

"Go directly under the falls, swim straight in and come up slowly," he warned, placing his hand on his head. He had to shout to be heard above the roar. "I'll go in first and be there to make sure you don't hit your head on the travertine. Don't worry, it's a piece of cake."

He must have noticed my look of terror as I treaded water and looked at the enormous flow of water coming down the thirty-five foot chute. Dean was born and lived all his life on a lake in Michigan. He was at home in water, and had been to the Green Room many times before. I, on the other hand, remember being afraid of the water when I was a kid. One day, when I was about twelve years old, my family was visiting friends who lived on a lake. I was playing on a very unstable raft when one of my sisters pushed me into deep water. I looked down and saw nothing but dark water and weeds reaching up to snare an ankle and drag me to my watery grave. It took many years to overcome the fear I acquired that day.

I watched Dean, a roar sounding like a jet engine pounding in my ears. I dove directly under the hydrologic chaos, my heart racing. All I could hear was the pounding of water on water above me, and all I could see was nothing, liquid darkness.

I panicked and immediately headed to the surface. Wrong move. Now I was directly in the chaos. Foaming, frothing white water, with so much air I had no purchase, no way to kick out. In that moment I thought I was going to die. Slight exaggeration. In seconds I was pushed out by the force of the plunging water coming down. My heart was still racing, and as I allowed the current to carry me around the eddy, I caught hold of the roots of a tree growing right out of the pool, and remained there for a couple of minutes until my heart returned to normal. Tenuously, I pushed out, found the current, and swam towards the falls.

Even though I was scared, I wanted to do this. The memory of leaving the jumping rock while regretting my decision not to jump motivated me to try again. I took a deep breath and again returned to the world under the falls. Doing several frog-kicks moved me deeper into the darkness. I was starting to feel anxious, but then saw a hint of light above me. Still underwater, I could actually see Dean outlined against the roof of the cave. I rose slowly and surfaced. I took a gratifyingly deep breath. This time it really was a deep breath. I smiled.

"I was just getting ready to go looking for you. What took you so long?"

I told him about my misadventure and he congratulated me for having the courage to try again. I was both relieved and happy I had done it. Too many times in my life I had turned around and gone back, regretting it later, as I had with the jump. Maybe this was a new chapter. I could use this experience in the future to keep me going when I might want to turn back.

It was amazing. The reflection of the sun off the bottom of the pool cast a green light into the cave giving it its distinctive name, the Green Room. Stalactites covered the ceiling. It felt like a watery cocoon. For several minutes I just looked around stunned, and then a shiver went through me. Without the warming effects of the sun, I suddenly realized I was freezing. I crossed my arms, grabbing opposite shoulders and shook. Dean understood the body language and gestured to the right. Evidently there was another way out. He jumped in and swam away looking part fish and part human. I followed, ducking the rocks overhead, and surfaced about twenty feet to the left of the falls. On the shore people were smiling and clapping. We later heard they had become concerned when they didn't see us for a time.

Several others had to see the Green Room, and we spent another hour playing in the area. Marian climbed up the far side of the cascade to show us another pool, and yet another pool above that. It was a tropical hideaway. It was too bad we had to go back. It would have been amazing to spend the night here, listening to the music of the water, soaking up the negative ions floating off the falls. Although

I didn't realize it at the time, I would indeed sleep near that wonderful pool on a future trip. But that's another story.

Marian reluctantly rose from her sunning spot beside the highest pool. "It's about time," she said, interrupting my thoughts. A couple of others that had joined us rose also and began heading down. Turning, she looked at me. I hadn't moved.

"Coming Charly?" she asked.

"In a couple of minutes. Go on. I'll catch up," I said.

She waved and continued.

My thoughts turned to reflect on the trip and how it was affecting me. There was certainly a timelessness to the Canyon. Where humans think in centuries and consider that a long time, the Canyon is a place where a century is a tick on the evolutionary clock. I had been walking in and on rock that is over five hundred million years old. If you removed one human lifetime from history, it would mean very little in the big picture. But it would mean a lot to the humans who lived that lifetime.

Out loud I asked the Universe in general, "Why are we here? Is it to make our mark somehow? Contribute to the gene pool? Leave the world a better place for having been in it? What's the point if we are such a small speck in an infinite time and space?"

The Canyon had forced me to slow down. I had spent the first 35 years of my life trying to fit in; trying to find happiness outside myself, through relationships with the "right" woman; displaying my skills in work, having the "right" house in the "right" neighborhood. The fact that I had fallen short in all those areas was testimony to the futility I'd felt before coming here.

Now I was wearing shorts, walking in funky sneakers, living 24 hours a day outdoors, peeing in the river, existing communally with twenty-one very diverse human beings, and I was the happiest I had ever been. What was the key to my happiness? I certainly wasn't demonstrating any great skill or intellectual acumen, there was no woman hanging on my arm to testify to my manly attractiveness, and I wasn't earning a penny. How could I be so happy, so content with so little?

"You are finally digging deeper, Charly. Your questions are from your soul, from the heart of who you are." It was Spirit Dancer broadcasting inside my head. "Your experiences here have caused you to remove the costumes you have been wearing most of your life."

"What costumes? This isn't a theater, Spirit Dancer, this is life."

"Ah, what is life but a play, with you being the writer, producer and star. Wasn't it one of your revered playwrights who said all life is a stage and we but actors in it? In truth you all wear costumes. For most of you there is no recognition of that fact. You think the clothes you wear reflect who you are. In fact your clothes are merely the veneer covering a body that is a shell that contains the inner workings of a human being.

"Here you are an awakening human, coming from a life of struggle, immersed in an environment that is connected to the bigger picture of life. This is a good metaphor for you."

"How so? I don't get the connection."

"Thus far your life has been primarily a day-to-day struggle. You struggle from paycheck to paycheck, you struggle to figure out who you are, why you're here, how you can find happiness in a world that is increasingly chaotic. The struggle is not in what you seek, but in how you go about it."

"Meaning what?" I was getting that defensive, "I'm not good enough" feeling.

"It's not helpful to feel attacked. I'm only stating the truth that you have already acknowledged. Defending, and the actions that stem from that, namely justifying, merely keep you stuck. Do you want to hear more?" Her tone was firm and communicated no sympathy for my discomfort.

"Just a moment ago I was practically in ecstasy and thoroughly enjoying myself. Then you showed up and things got heavy. This introspection stuff can be a drag sometimes."

"If you're looking for sympathy, you came to the wrong place. Life *is*, Charly. You are the filter through which it travels, and you determine how you perceive it and how you feel about it. Right now you're falling into the trap many humans do, the trap of wanting to be comfortable and happy. If you stay at that level of consciousness, it's okay, but you won't achieve what you want.

"You make a mistake when you assume life is meant to be comfortable. On the contrary, it is not. There is no guarantee of comfort in the natural world. Just change, and the constant drive for balance. Of course, you can create comfort in your life. If you're attached to it, you'll also create denial. That's where you don't know, and you don't want to know. Right now you're experiencing the dynamic tension of confusion. Confusion is a powerful state to be in, so long as you don't stay there."

"How can confusion be a powerful state to be in?" I couldn't wait for this answer.

"Simple. When you're confused, it means you're paying attention, you're becoming conscious of the circumstances in your life. On the learning curve it's known as conscious incompetence — you know you don't know. It's both painful and powerful because at this point you're aware things aren't the way you want them to be and you're motivated to do something to change the situation. All you have to do is take responsibility, and recognize the choices you have made in the past have created your current circumstances. Do you understand this?"

"Not totally. What's the power in recognizing the pain of my past choices?"

"Recognizing the pain of your past choices is merely judgment. That's not what I'm referring to here. No one will create the life they want if they don't first take responsibility for the choices they make and the outcomes they get. Instead of taking it as a negative judgment on yourself, accept your role in creating where you are. When you do that, freedom is around the bend, because now you can uncreate what you have created, and recreate what you want."

"Can you give me an example? I'm still not clear on what you're saying." I was grasping for something to help me understand what was obviously an important concept.

"You have a good one right on this trip. Remember how Jane was when you first met her?"

"Sure. She was scared, tentative, convinced she was going to die. What's the connection?"

"The connection is with all her fear, she was here. She was taking responsibility for her choice and willing to go where she'd never been. Because of that she got new information that helped her shift out of her fear, and take the support you offered her to develop more confidence in her own capability. Remember the motto, 'you've got to do it yourself, but you don't have to do it alone?'"

I nodded. Spirit Dancer continued.

"Jane took back her power to make good/bad, right/wrong choices. And she tapped into a deep reservoir of courage and ability she forgot she had."

"Forgot she had? How do you forget what you don't know you have?" It seemed like a logical question to me.

"Learning is remembering what you have forgotten. When Jane was born, she was perfect. She had within her the seeds of who she is, and access to infinite intelligence. Then she forgot. By coming to the Canyon, she placed herself far outside her comfort zone, and through her experiences reclaimed her power. She wouldn't have done that if she had continued to live a life devoted to comfort. In her discomfort she uncreated her belief she couldn't do certain things with her body. And she re-created a woman who was competent and willing to learn how to use her body to go where she wanted. Do you see what I'm saying here?"

"I do. So instead of worrying about what I don't have, what I haven't accomplished, what I can't do, I can move beyond all that by focusing on how I want things to be. By being willing to go where I've never been before, I can change my experience. Tell me more." I was now fully present and very curious.

"If you don't like what you are getting in your life, you have to un-create it by first determining how you want it to be. In order to do that you have to get out ahead of yourself, much like architects do when they design something new. Like John F. Kennedy did in the sixties when he declared the United States would put a man on the moon before the end of the decade. And it happened, in spite of the fact that at the time of his pronouncement there was no existing capability to accomplish such a monumental task.

"So, to go where you've never been before, go where you've never been before."

"Excuse me? Is that redundant?" I was half joking.

"Not at all," Spirit Dancer replied, showing no sign of impatience. "To create the life you don't have now requires you to get out ahead of yourself, wave the magic wand, so-to-speak, and declare, like JFK, how you want it to be. And don't make it practical, possible, or realistic."

"What do you mean, don't make it realistic?" That one had me stumped.

"Charly, have you ever had someone say to you, be realistic, you can't do that?"

"Yes, I have. When I was a freshman in college, I wanted to go out for the baseball team. It was a major university and I was still quite small, weighing less than 120 pounds. Several of my dorm-mates looked at me as if I was crazy when I told them I was planning to go out for the team. But I made it, won a freshman letter, and then played on an NCAA championship team the next year."

"And you wouldn't have had that incredible experience if you had been realistic, would you?"

"No."

"So, get out ahead of yourself, decide what you want, and then come back to your present reality and be brutally honest about where you are. From that information you can make wise choices about taking the steps to get from where you are to where you want to be."

We were at the last crossing and five minutes away from the boats, and I needed a starting point, so I asked Spirit Dancer how I should begin.

"First spend some time over the next day focused on your purpose. I know you think you don't know what it is, but you do. Just remember, your soul only has one desire for you, and that is to discover and express who you are. Begin with that, and then you can start waving the magic wand. I'll check in with you before the end of the trip." Then she was gone, eating and running, or should I say tantalizing me and running.

At any rate, I had no time to think about my purpose or anything else because everyone was cooperating with the guides so we could get downstream. We had to untie the boats, and one by one they had to pull out of the Hava-zoo parking lot, break through a strong, downstream current, avoiding the wall on the left. As soon as we were on the river, I would get out my journal and record what I had just experienced or I would forget something important. I decided to look at my purpose in the evening or morning. I knew we would have over twenty miles of flat water before running the last major rapid, called Lava Falls. So there would be plenty of time to think about this before our last adrenaline rush. It had been a full day and we still had ten miles to go before making camp.

Chapter Sixteen

Lava Day

Ah, the best laid plans of mice and men . . . I really had planned to look at my purpose after dinner. But Mother Nature intervened. We were camped at National Canyon, river mile 165 1/2. Dinner was great as usual. Everybody was sharing notes about the day. Those who hiked all the way to Mooney Falls, the younger and more vigorous of the group, were talking about the impressive falls and the thunderous thrill of climbing behind it. Some heard about my challenge with the Green Room and wanted more lurid details. The rest shared their meanderings which usually involved finding a shade spot by the river and sleeping between food and swimming. It was indeed a day spent in paradise.

As we were finishing up washing the dishes, the low rumblings of thunder invaded our ear space. At first it was soft and distant. Gradually the sounds grew louder and closer. Thunder is different in the Canyon than I remember back in the Midwest. It is softer, not as jarring. The vibrations bounce off the Canyon's walls, and degrade as they roll up or downstream. It reminds me of kettle drums in an orchestra. An initial report and then drum rolls.

Where there is thunder there will inevitably be lightening. And this light show began with flashes of white light illuminating the darkening sky, back lighting the canyon walls above us. The first drops of rain arrived just behind a strong upstream wind. The rush was on. In unison there was a stampede for the tent bag.

Putting up the tents in strong winds must have looked like a scene from a Three Stooges movie. First the poles had to be strung together, then threaded through external sleeves. This is challenging enough on a calm day, let alone in gusting winds at night. Again the guides eased the road for us. Each bolt of lightning and crack of thunder was accompanied by hoops and hollers from the guides, bringing a spirit of adventure to the group. The air was pregnant with electrical charges mixed with excitement.

Finally all the tents were up. Instead of seeking shelter from the rain, most of us put on our rain jackets and stood around waiting for the next bolt. The rain increased in intensity and then we saw it. It was a huge surge of water, highlighted by a brilliant lightning flash, just across the river from our camp. The spout was, it turned out, one of many pouring out of the canyon walls up and down the river.

In the desert, there is nothing to hold water back. No grasses and thickets of shrubs, no significant forests of trees to soak up the water. Just hard pan desert soil, plants and cacti, most with shallow root systems that are easily uprooted and carried along in surges of water that build in intensity as it picks up more debris. The sight of a water spout shooting out of the canyon wall and carrying over fifty feet before plunging into the Colorado is awesome and exciting.

No one would sleep much that night, and no one seemed to care. The intensity of the storm never let up. It seemed as if the storm cell was directly overhead, locked in on us. The rains would come in waves, increasing in intensity as the winds whipped up the desert soil and mixed it with the swirling rain into an emulsion that coated everything and would leave its calling card as a dirty residue after the water evaporated in the dry desert air. Then the rain would disappear for long periods of time, giving the lightning and thunder equal time on center stage. I tried to sleep several times, only to be roused by another round of strobe-like flashes and high decibel sound effects. Finally, exhausted, I fell into a restless sleep.

In the early morning light, I emerged from my tent to discover a river half again as high as it was before the storm. The waterfalls and flash flooding from the side streams had pushed eight thousand cubic feet per second of additional water into the channel.

Marian had told me Lava would be running around fourteen thousand cubic feet per second, which she described as a great level to run the right side.

"It's over twenty thousand," I overheard Dean saying to Wally. They were in the kitchen preparing coffee. "Makes the right side marginal. We might have to go left." They were discussing the run at Lava. Wally nodded, and smiled, "Marginal, but what a kick, eh?" Obviously there would be a decision to make as to the best run. Safety is always the first priority in the Canyon, but that doesn't mean that going for the gusto is out. The guides would wait to see the rapid before making a decision on their run.

Lava day is always filled with tension because it is the last and most notorious of the major rapids in the Canyon. During the trip, the guides would talk of Lava in near mythic terms. It didn't take long before the passengers were comparing everything to their image of Lava, as if they were the experts. Lava is the rapid by which all others are measured. The last couple of days on the river had been very mellow, like the calm before, and in this case, after, the storm. Today there was some added tension due to the unknown effects of last night's rain and subsequent flooding.

As was true when we ran Hance and the two days in the big water of the inner gorge, this morning the guides were more serious and focused on rigging their boats. They made certain all straps were tied down tighter than normal, and that there were no loose straps flying around that could capture a leg and trap someone underwater in the event of a flip. "Rigging for flipping" is the term they used. Not that they expected to flip. On the contrary, in over two hundred trips run collectively by the members of the crew, there had only been five flips.

I was again on James' boat, and the only passenger. We were going to have our longest river day yet, twenty eight miles. But James said it shouldn't be a problem because the current would be strong from the higher water level.

There was no morning talk except Greg outlining the activities of the day: thirteen miles to Lava, stop and scout, run the rapid, have lunch, and float another fifteen miles to camp at mile 194. Without any unforeseen delays, we could get to camp fairly early.

Floating on water that was colored a rich red/brown was a little disconcerting. It was less like water, and more like some viscous, roiling red bean soup. The water was no longer friendly. In fact, it felt angry and threatening. James said this was how the pre-dam Colorado looked. "Too thin to plow, too thick to drink", as the saying of old river runners went.

All of a sudden everything was different. Before the flood, we could take water out of the river, run it through a filter, and drink it. Some of the guides drank water without filtering it. Here's how James described what we would be doing after we got to camp:

"We'll have to settle the sediment out in five gallon buckets, aided by sprinkling alum powder that will attract the sediment as it falls to the bottom of the bucket. Then we'll decant the clear water before running it through the filter. To be extra safe, a little chlorine will be added to kill any viruses that might be present." The thought of drinking water containing chlorine sent a chill down my spine. I know it's in all treated municipal water, but I won't drink it if I can taste it. I may have no choice now.

We were now in one of the longest quiet stretches of the Canyon. The walls rose almost three thousand feet above us in steep stair step fashion, closing us in and focusing our attention on the quiet river. It was as if nature was conspiring to add further drama to the reputation of Lava Falls. I decided to take advantage of thirteen miles of calm waters and dug my journal out of my dry bag. I began to write:

"SD has suggested I explore my purpose for being here, on this planet, in this body. She gave me a clue: my soul only has one desire for me, and that is to discover and express who I am. So that must be my purpose. But that can't be it; or at least it can't be the whole thing. So what if I discover and express who I am? Ah, there's got to be a 'so what?' in here. Let's say it this way: My purpose is to discover and express who I am so that . . ."

Then my mind went blank. I tried again.

"My purpose is to discover and express who I am so that . . ."

Again, nothing. Aaargh! This whole exercise reminded me of the feeling of powerlessness I had experienced many times in my life. Whenever I tried to figure out what I wanted to do or be, I would come up with blanks. It was as if my mind went into a state of suspended animation where it was no longer able to function.

Then I heard Spirit Dancer in my head.

"Talk about it, Charly. Think out loud."

At first I felt embarrassed, ashamed actually. How could I talk about this with James there? I'd be admitting my weaknesses, and feel foolish.

"Who's responsible for your life, Charly?" It was Spirit Dancer again, prodding me to go where I've never been before. I remembered what she had said yesterday about getting out ahead of myself, waving the magic wand, so to speak. So I swallowed hard, and opened my mouth.

"I need to think out loud, if you don't mind, James."

"Help yourself, Charly."

"I'm trying to figure out what my purpose is, what I'm here to do. It's a real challenge. So far I've come up with one piece—to discover and be who I am. But there's at least one more piece and it's what I'm calling the 'so what' piece. So what if I discover and express who I am? How is that going to make a difference?"

"Sounds like Don Quixote to me, Charly."

"What do you mean? What does Don Quixote have to do with this?"

"He spent his whole life seeking himself, always looking outside himself for his meaning and purpose. He didn't realize until too late that he missed most of his life by looking in the wrong places. What's wrong with just living life as it comes, enjoying the experiences, learning what you can, and sharing whatever you have with others? I never understood why people put their lives on hold seeking answers to eternal questions like 'Who am I?' and 'Why am I here?' Seems like a real waste of energy and time to me."

This certainly wasn't what I expected or even wanted to hear. James' argument made a lot of sense. I knew others besides myself who seemed to have their lives on hold waiting for answers to these eternal questions. Is this all smoke and mirrors? Maybe there isn't any value in knowing why we're here. Are we wrong?

"There is no right or wrong, Charly. But there are consequences to the choices we make and don't make." It was Spirit Dancer with another remote broadcast. "What James is saying has value, especially for people who put their lives on hold waiting for the perfect anything, including the perfect purpose. Everyone has a purpose for being here. For some it can appear very grandiose, for others quite simple. Some people are very conscious of describing their purpose and living a life that is congruent; others pay no attention to the description, they just live a purposeful life. Many don't do either, living from one day to the next making ends meet, hoping for the best. One is not better than the other, just different.

"You, like everyone else, have to trust your own inner guidance. Remember, what's right is what works. Self doubt is the obstacle to that trust. Self acceptance and self love are the solutions. By accepting who you are, telling the truth about it and acting out of that truth, everything else will fall into place. Think about it, Charly. Look at the choices you have made in your life. The relationships you've been in, the work you've done, the experiences you've had. Which ones have been most valuable?"

I thought about my relationships and saw that the most valuable ones were with women I met spontaneously, where I didn't try to make anything happen. The relationships that were least satisfying were the ones I tried to force. I looked at my work and realized all my adult jobs were an attempt to fit into what I thought I "should" do, not what I loved to do. And the experiences that have been most valuable, working on the ranches in Montana, fishing trips in Canada, my internship in Holland during business school, winning an NCAA baseball championship, and so on, were more like gifts that came to me. They were things I was interested in, but didn't struggle to make happen. Often they came as invitations or suggestions.

"For the most part, I see what you're getting at. Almost all the meaningful relationships and experiences I've had fit who I am. They came naturally, often effortlessly. I didn't have to plan or scheme, or think about it too much. Is it possible I think too much?"

"What do you think?" I could imagine the smile on Spirit Dancer's face with that ironic response. "Look, Charly, there's nothing wrong with your mind or thinking. In fact, you have a very well developed mind and it has served you well. But the intellect often becomes limiting when it is relied on too much. We have to learn to bring it into a reasonable balance with our feelings and our instincts. A big part of your challenge is to trust those feelings and instincts so you can take advantage of the opportunities that present themselves to you. You've missed some big ones in the past, you know."

"What big ones? How could I miss them?"

"What is not important. How you missed them is by being in your head too much of the time. Being too rational, logical and realistic. Doing what you thought was the correct thing to do. Remember the Wheel of Effortless Energy? Stop sacrificing, tap into your receptive, intuitive nature, align with the information that you 'hear', and trust yourself and the process.

"It's really very simple. The Puzzle Theory says what's right is what works, at the feeling level! Your life is filled with a lot that has worked for you, but your intellect is not satisfied because it hasn't fit the picture on the outside of your box. You can trust me on this one, Charly. There are a lot of great opportunities coming your way. All you have to do is say yes when they come along."

"Okay, let me try this on for size. My soul only has one desire for me, and that is to be who I am. It doesn't matter what I do, specifically, so long as it fits my values and I choose to do it. So being who I am is merely knowing myself well enough to respond to what is available all the time. It's not about coming up with some fancy purpose statement. It's being able to enjoy life right here, right now."

"The purpose statement you might create is merely a verbal, intellectual description of how you live your life at the feeling level, Charly. Very few people actually take the time to put something like that on paper. Many of them have good lives because they live from their feeling awareness. Others would benefit from having a clear statement because it helps them be focused. The important thing is knowing when you're living on purpose and when you are not."

"How will I know?" I started to ask. "Wait, I know what you're going to say. I'll know at the feeling level, right?"

"Correct, my friend. When you are on purpose, life becomes an effort-less experience. You don't have to work as hard to be successful, people and things seem to come to you without your even seeking them, opportunities arrive as gifts through suggestions, observations, invitations. When you're not in alignment with your purpose, you will notice more stress, more effort on your part, and less support from the world around you. It's difficult for the logical mind to accept that life can operate in this manner, but if you look at your experiences, I know you will see its validity."

From somewhere in the distance I heard James' voice interrupting my daydream.

"This is Vulcan's Anvil, Charly," he remarked. "It's a volcanic plug formed within the last 250,000 years during a lava flow. The Indians consider it a sacred object. The Hualapais believe one of their most powerful shamen in the early 19th century received his power from it."

As we floated closer to this monument to nature's recycling process, the anvil loomed larger. It stood perhaps fifty feet out of the water and was about thirty feet wide. On the top was a cactus garden growing out of the blue-black lava, with prickly pear cactus and desert grasses, all deposited by birds relieving themselves as they flew by. James threw a coin high up on the Anvil as we glided by.

"Why did you do that?" I asked, wondering if it was some kind of guide superstition.

"It's just a tradition. We throw a coin to the Anvil, and if it sticks on it, then we'll have a good run in Lava."

Lava! In my calm reverie I had forgotten all about the grand-daddy of the rapids. All of a sudden I was aware of some anxiety and the need to relieve myself. We were still a mile upstream of the rapid, in what James called Lava Lake, the calm, slow water stretch above all the big rapids. I sat uncomfortably on the front tube of the raft looking downstream, wondering when I would see and hear this monster. As we floated closer, I became more nervous. Not hearing or seeing any evidence of it made things even more tense. James was very quiet, which fed my anxiety.

We were coming around a point on the right side of the river, and all of a sudden the sound of Lava came rushing upstream. Someone had just turned off the mute button and the volume was up very high. Not only was it loud, but it had by far the deepest, lowest growl of any of the rapids we had run. I could see where the sound was coming from, but could see no river past a certain point, an indication of a severe drop. In fact, Lava is relatively short and very intense, dropping thirty-seven feet in less than a quarter mile.

The bar had just been raised. Frivolity had disappeared. The guides all had business-like faces and purposeful strides as we walked along a trail leading to our scouting rock overlooking the rapid. We walked up a steep incline that wandered through an intensely hot field of lava debris. "If it's this hot here, imagine how hot it must be for those triathletes who have to ride a bike 110 miles through the lava fields in Hawaii," I said to no one in particular.

The "scout rock" was a large piece of lava just upstream of the entrance to Lava Falls, a rapid created by debris flows coming out of Prospect Canyon above the rapid and on the left side of the river. James told me there had been at least nine lava flows in the past million years which had dammed the river. At least one created a dam over two thousand feet high, backing the river up into Utah over two hundred miles upstream.

The guides were all assembled in a group, going through their scout ritual which involved watching the rapid and pointing at specific markers like current lines or waves or holes. The entry into Lava on the right side is actually seventeen feet lower than the normal river level and there is no way to see where it is, so the guides have to line up on a current line that comes off a large lava boulder about one hundred feet upstream. The current line isn't straight, and as I watched it, it seemed to travel out almost to the middle of the river before being pulled by some invisible magnetic force to the right and down the tongue into the maelstrom.

Set up is crucial, because below the entry waves is a giant "V" wave, formed by two diagonal waves that come together in the shape of a "V". James said most boats will fill up with water in that section, and it was crucial to enter straight and with momentum.

It was time to go. The guides formed into a tight circle, placed their hands on top of one another, and as their hands raised overhead, their voices climbed in unison peaking in a primal scream of solidarity. We walked back to the boats, somber and nervous. Periodically the guides would look back at the rapid as if trying to remember the run. When we arrived at the boats, there were instructions about extra tight life jackets, holding on, following the guides' directions. There was also much more attention to making sure everything was secure than in any other rapid. It wasn't only the guides who had cotton mouth.

We would be running fourth behind Greg, Marian and Wally, with Dean behind us. At first the current was very slow, adding to the tension. As we approached the large boulder to pick up on the current line, the pace picked up. I watched as first Greg, then Marian and Dean dropped into the rapid, literally falling out of sight as they slid down the tongue to the entry waves seventeen feet below. Watching them disappear didn't slow down my accelerating heart rate any.

The sound of this huge monster was deafening as we climbed the marker wave at the top of the rapid. It had looked inconsequential from the scout rock, but on the river it turned out to be surprisingly large. How big are the waves that already looked big, I wondered? I was afraid James was too far left. The current seemed to latch onto the boat, dragging it towards the middle of the river and the feared ledge hole that eagerly awaited any errant boat and its passengers.

Suddenly the current reversed direction and we started to slide down the glassy tongue.

"Hold on, Charly," James screamed, barely competing with the thunder around us. "When we enter the "V" wave, throw your weight into the front tube!" He didn't have to tell me to hold on. My white knuckles already extended all the way to my elbows.

It looked like we were plunging into hell. The diagonal waves raced alongside the boat, towering above us on either side, drawing us to the point of no return that looked like a bottomless pit.

We hit the intersection of both waves with a jarring thud, and for an instant seemed to be suspended in liquid space. Water poured over me, engulfing the entire raft. For an instant we were in the void, darkness with no sense of up, down, or out. Then light reached through my watery mask and we appeared below the "V" wave picking up speed as we raced towards the oversized wave at the bottom of the rapid.

Some people call the rock behind the wave the cheese grater for its capacity to shred anyone who mistakenly gets too close. We were a little right of center and our boat was angled slightly left as we slid down the swell. James was working frantically to turn the boat so we would climb the wave at the correct angle. The water rose above us like a sleeping giant stretching after a long slumber. Our boat rose up the curling surface and peaked at the top, shuddering and deciding whether it was our time to flip or not.

Not. We slid over the top of the wave and raced past the cheese grater, which seemed to reach out trying to pull us into its embrace. James let out a loud whoop, celebrating his successful run and releasing hours of pent-up tension. "ABL," he shouted exultantly, "alive below Lava!" We slapped hands and I reached for the bailing bucket to begin the task of relieving the raft of some 300 gallons of water. We still had Son of Lava to run just downstream.

The rest of the day was mellow by comparison. Lunch was prepared below Son of Lava. The crew swapped tales of their runs, passengers joined in with their views, and a hard boiled egg was tossed into the current in a ritual of thanks to the River Gods for another injury-free run. Greg relaxed because we were below the point of danger on the trip, and the afternoon was an easy float to camp at mile 194.

That night we celebrated. The guides got out their most outrageous costumes, passengers improvised, all the remaining drinks were combined into a five gallon bucket, and frivolity abounded. The next day we enjoyed a mellow float along a verdant river corridor with many birds serenading us on our way. We ran three decent sized rapids, but they paled in comparison to the mighty Lava Falls. If we had run those rapids on day one, we would have been anxious. Now we had to caution against being too blasé.

Chapter Seventeen

Last Camp

Our last camp, at mile 220, provided one of our biggest skies. The Colorado is very wide and the canyon walls are recessed far back presenting us with an impressive vista. After dinner, everyone pitched in, helping the guides load everything but personal gear and the bathroom "unit" back on the boats.

Nathan asked why we were loading the boats now rather than at our usual time after breakfast, and Greg responded that he would explain after the task was completed. It took no less than twenty minutes. Two weeks ago we were all strangers, coming from different places and different lives. Now we were like a tribe, working together with mutual respect and cooperation. What other force can bring people together in such a short time with no effort, I remember thinking.

Finally, Greg asked everyone to form a circle. The fading light offered a black on gray silhouette of the darkening canyon walls standing proudly against a sky holding onto the day's color.

"Thank you all for your help," Greg began softly, as if any volume would betray fragile emotions. "Not only for tonight, but throughout this trip. You've made our jobs easier and more enjoyable.

"We loaded the boats tonight, because tomorrow is our last morning and we like to end our trips with a silent float. We'll be getting up earlier than usual. It will still be dark when we wake you up, and we ask that you get everything in your black bags and down to the boats as quickly as possible with the least amount of talking you can manage.

"We will have coffee for you and there will be time to use the unit before we shove off. Once we get on the river," he continued, his voice low and gentle, "we will be in silence. The float will allow you to listen to and watch the Canyon wake up. Our passengers often tell us it is one of the highlights of the trip."

He then switched gears. "As a crew, our job is to offer you the opportunity to experience this place as fully as possible. Over the years we have all seen the impact the Canyon has on people's lives, and are always interested in gaining insight into your experiences—your perceptions of this place and its impact on you. This is a time for looking back upstream and reflecting on our time together.

"For those who are so inclined, I would like to hear what gifts you have received from the Canyon. Maybe it is a new appreciation for the natural world, or some new awareness, a lesson, or just a chance to relax.

"I always learn something on my trips. This trip helped me see the value and necessity of honoring the transition of people going out and the new people coming in. I know it made it easier to let go of Richard and the others who left at Phantom. It also made it better for the Chances to become part of us more quickly.

"Would anyone else like to talk about their experience?"

There was an awkward moment of silence, and then Jane spoke. In almost reverent tones she thanked the guides for the "most significant experience of my life."

"My friends thought I was crazy when I told them of my plans to raft the Grand Canyon. On the first day, I wished I had listened to them. But after the first couple of rapids I realized I wasn't going to die. Then something happened during our hike in North Canyon, and it was like a light turning on.

"After Charly helped me over that ledge, I knew I could do more than I thought. I know how simple that must sound to you, but it was a big deal for me. I had been helping others, especially my mom, for so long. I forgot what it was like to ask for help. Now I look forward to more challenges and I know if I can't do it alone, I can find the help I need to go where I want. Thank you everybody, for being there for me."

A lump formed in my throat as Jane spoke, and I wasn't alone. As I looked around the circle, I could see several people wiping tears from their eyes.

The mood was shattered by Frank's booming voice. "On a more pragmatic note, I have to say this has been one of the best vacations I've ever had. I've been all over the world and haven't found anything like what the Grand Canyon offers. It has it all, except frozen daiquiris," he said, waiting for people to laugh. We didn't.

"Seriously, though," he continued, a hint of insecurity betraying his sense of self control, "what I will remember most about this trip is the incredible richness and diversity down here. That hike in Saddle amazed me, especially when we walked through so many riparian zones and then I discovered the Dobson fly life cycle in just a few yards.

"I'll be heading back to work feeling rested and invigorated. Heck, I just realized I haven't even thought about work since the trip began. That's a first."

I was glad he hadn't gone off on some extended monologue, and while I don't think I'll ever seek him out, I was glad to hear him speak so positively about his experience. I uttered a silent thank you for the lessons I had learned from this tyrant.

Then Nathan spoke up, tentatively at first, but quickly assuming that child-like enthusiasm we had all come to love. Nathan had become everyone's little brother, or son.

"Um, I liked this trip very much.....This place is like a big playground." Laughter surged around our circle like a phonetic wave, relaxing everyone. "I liked the desserts," another round of laughter, "paddling in the ducky, the hikes, and Lava was my favorite rapid. The only thing I didn't like was having to carry all those black bags (waterproof bags containing clothing and sleep gear) to the camps my parents picked. One was so far away, I thought I would turn eleven before I got all the bags to camp."

We all shook with laughter at that image. No ordinary ten year old, this one.

"We will cherish this trip for the rest of our lives, " added Fran Chance, a laugh still on her lips. "Jack, Jesse, Nathan and I want to thank you all for providing the vacation of a lifetime. One we will certainly look back on often. We are so impressed with you guides. I felt very safe, even that first day in Horn, Granite, Hermit and Crystal. And Greg is right, it was easier to become a part of the group because of our little ceremony that first night.

"I have never seen people work so hard, so long, and for that matter, so well together. I don't know how you find the energy to do everything you do and manage to be smiling all the time. It certainly says volumes about your love for the Canyon and your work. I'm glad my children had a chance to see models of people doing what they love. Thank you . . . for everything."

"I used to be a teacher," Dean chimed in after a few moments of silence. "Got burned out. Down here I get to share the Canyon and let it do the teaching. I hope you will take some of your new awareness back with you and apply it in your homes and your communities. Things like respecting the earth, conserving water, recycling, being out in nature, facing challenges, working together. They all apply equally well back home. Take some of the Canyon with you, just not the rocks," he finished with a chuckle.

Laughter again spread throughout the circle. If it had been light enough, we would undoubtedly have seen some guilty expressions from those who had a rock or three packed in their black bag.

"I am always heartened by the courage my passengers demonstrate," interjected Marian in her upbeat, caring voice. "This trip is no exception. I won't identify you because I don't want to embarrass anyone. But I want to acknowledge you for going where you've never been, for facing your fears, and moving ahead when part of you wanted to turn back. We can all do so much more than we think, and your examples fortify me when I face my own challenges.

"To add to what Dean said, I hope you will remember what you have seen and heard regarding the issues around water. For those of you from the North and East, water seems so abundant you probably don't think about having to conserve it. If so, please remember we are all part of a system, local, regional, national and global. What we do does impact others. What you conserve, which you can do with little or no inconvenience to yourself, is then available to others who have less." Again there was a moment of silence, with people nodding their heads in agreement as they looked around the circle.

"There is no way I can describe in words what the Canyon means to me," Wally intoned, in his playfully serious voice. "Periodically I receive a letter from a passenger that says it so well that I want to share those words with others. Here is one that I really love, and says it better than I ever could. It's from a passenger from my first trip a couple of years ago.

"I remember sounds, sounds of running water in a stony land. Swirls and spots and veins in ancient pink granite as old as the earth. The green scent of creeks in side canyons and the odd smell of the ocean in the inner gorge. Near shadowed walls sliding across far high cliffs still bright in sunshine, and towers formed in ocean beds before dinosaurs walked on the earth, reflecting upside down in glassy pools.

"The green silk of the rapid's tongue fed us into a frenzy that sent foam above our heads, dousing us with tons of icy water; and ten seconds later we were drifting below the rapid, watching broken light dancing in the current.

"We learned to love twenty people we had never known before, and shared jokes, and wished we never had to lose them. To see rafts behind and ahead of us, seemed all the friendship we could ever need. The narrow section of river and slice of sky all the world there was. The isolation from news right and proper.

"There are lessons that apply in other places. No rapid looks big . . . until you're in the middle of it. You don't need what you thought you did lying on sand watching stars wheel overhead, listening to the haunting call of the Great Horned Owl echoing off the cliffs. There is a strong sense of the planet and of deep time you know you should keep. You listen to the delicate rippling of the powerful river, and determine you should likewise be quiet about what you are. And separate from any responsibility other than to yourself, you remember your childhood freedom and wonder, whether it was necessary to lose it."

A profound silence swept over us as Wally's voice trailed off. With a canopy of stars blanketing the moonless sky, and the soft voice of the river reflecting our metaphorical life journey, Wally 's words had enfolded us like the nurturing aroma of fresh bread baking in the oven.

After a long meditative silence, Hub surprised us by speaking. Throughout most of the trip, he was conspicuous by his silence. He was one of the men from Texas. Sixty-six years old and a retired auto dealer, he seemed to be having a good time, but he wasn't very vocal about it.

"I'm a pretty quiet guy. Don't see a lot of value in words. But I appreciate the friendships that formed on this trip and I have a poem I'd like to read that says it better than I could. It's called "A Rare Find", and was written by a poet named Randall Rieman.

"It's a wonderful thing,
Though it's hard to explain,
When you meet a new friend on your way,
And you know, in no time,
There's a reason behind
The ease that your friendship's obtained;
For your spirits are one,
Though your friendship's begun
Only just a few hours ago;
Yet the things that you share
And the feelin' that's there
Is more lasting and precious than gold.

"Well, your talk ran from cattle
to horses, to shoeing,
To starting these colts on their way.
And before your own eyes
The time has flown by;
Adios is the thing you now say.
But you sure hate to go,
And your feelin's they show
On your face as you shake your friend's hand.

Still, you know that you're lucky
To have this new friend
Who shares your same love for the land,
For horses and cattle,
For life in the saddle
And nights underneath a clear sky.
A sameness in spirit that goes beyond words-
We share that, my new friend and I.

"As I lift up my head
From my old canvas bed,
I thank the good Lord for His care.
And for my new friend,
May we soon meet again,
For I know we have much more to share.
See, our spirits are one,
Though our friendship's begun
Only just a few hours ago.
Still, the things that we share
And the feelin' that's there
Is more lasting and precious than gold."

Another long silence hovered over our circle. It was as if we needed time to swallow the words, taste their flavor, and allow them to find a home within each of us. Our intimate circle was remarkable since all we had in common was a shared experience in the Grand Canyon.

No one else seemed to have anything to say. Maybe they were struggling with the right words, like I was at that moment. It was as if we needed some time to pass so the import of the experience could be fully savored and understood. I wanted to say the perfect thing, especially coming on the heels of those two poems.

"Don't think, Charly. Feel." Spirit Dancer's voice echoed in my head and loosened my locked jaw.

"I can't even begin to describe all that this trip has been for me. Maybe I never will take it all in, it is so immense. To say it has been enlightening would be an understatement.

"I've learned so much . . . about me . . . and others. It has been a pure pleasure being with all of you. I can't believe it's almost over. Seems like we just shoved off from Lees Ferry a couple of days ago. Oddly enough, it also feels like I've been gone from Michigan for months. There must be pixie dust in the air that suspends time in our minds.

"If there is one lesson I will take back home, it is to take personal responsibility for what I choose to do, and for the consequences of those choices. Before I came here, I now realize, I had been waiting for others to make me happy, successful, competent, at peace with myself.

"Spending time here has helped me realize that only I can do that for myself. So among all the other gifts, known and unknown, I've received from you all and from the Canyon, I will not forget this one.

"Oh, and if you decide to come back and do another trip, perhaps you'll see me here. I've decided I'm coming back, hopefully to become a guide. No matter what it takes."

The smiles and shouts of "Congratulations!" and "Go for it, Charly!" brought a warm glow to my gut and a tear to my eye. It was a loving gesture from my Canyon tribe. We had become a family, and now it was time to get some sleep. It was already dark, and our wake up call would come far too soon.

Most of us wandered off to our respective camp sites. A few remained huddled around Hub as he read more from his cowboy poetry book. I felt drained, physically and emotionally. I didn't want the trip to be end, and it was. I couldn't do anything to change that. So I rolled out my sleeping bag, stretched for a couple of minutes, laid on my back and looked at the canopy of silver stars etched into the black velvet ceiling. A shooting star streaked across the sky. It was the last thing I remembered that night.

Chapter Eighteen

Dawn
Float

Marian's soft voice removed me from a deep, satisfying slumber "We've got a little more than an hour, so get your gear loaded and use the unit, because the outhouse at the take-out is too gross for words. We'll be in silence once we get on the river. Remember to keep your conversations until then to a minimum and low volume."

I stretched my body as I lay in my bag, and looked up at the still night sky. Venus, the morning planet, was like a spotlight beaming her love to Earth. Sagittarius, the archer, was aiming his arrow at Antares, the heart of Scorpio. Signus, the swan, and Aquila, the eagle, were outlined in the almost cloud-like Milky Way, both pointed towards Scorpio. The velvet-black sky was dotted with silver lights of varying magnitudes. As I looked towards Polaris, the bright star at the end of the Little Dipper's handle, a bright streak slashed across the sky.

"The future awaits you, Charly. What you do today will determine what it will look and feel like. Are you awake enough to hear what I have to say?"

"Good morning to you, too, Spirit Dancer," I replied with a smile. "I thought you might show up today. I'd sure like to take a ride in your starship some time. What kind of mileage do you get?"

"Unlimited. But we don't have time for that right now. You've only got a few minutes to understand how important this morning is for you. I want your undivided attention so I can be sure you hear what I have to say. Do I make myself clear, Charly?"

"Eminently, Spirit Dancer. If you don't mind, I'll just pack my gear away while you give me my marching, er, I should say, floating, orders. I'm all ears."

"To paraphrase an old cliché', this is the last day of your old life, and the first day of your possible new life. You stand at a threshold, Charly. A choice point. This morning you can literally change your life in six short river miles. For that to happen, you must employ much of what you have learned during your time here in Grand Canyon. Do you hear what I'm telling you?"

"Loud and clear. What do I need to do?"

"Grow, Charly—up and out. This is just the beginning, but everything you do from now on will either contribute to the new beginning you want, or it will interfere with that new beginning. Remember I talked to you about transitions, and you communicated with Greg about endings and new beginnings?"

"Yes. So how does this morning float fit in with that?"

"The same way honoring those hiking out represented endings, and being conscious about those hiking in represented the recognition of new beginnings. You are not just floating the last six miles of your Grand Canyon trip, you are bringing the entire experience down here to a close. It is the perfect way to be conscious of what you have learned on this trip, and make some decisions about how you and your life will be different.

"My people were very conscious of the power of using ceremony to honor and acknowledge change. Your morning float can be just such a ceremony."

"I thought a ceremony was where you acknowledged someone who was retiring for their service, or where you congratulated someone for graduating from school. How is this float like that?"

"Ceremony is any opportunity to mark change. I define it as ritual with heart. It's not going through the motions, it's actually being conscious about the change you are honoring. In this case, you will have almost two hours this morning to bring closure to your trip. If you do it with your heart and your head, it will be very powerful." Spirit Dancer's words were very clear and pointed, as if she wanted me to pay extra attention.

"What do you want me to do?"

"If you want more freedom in your life, you have to be conscious all the time. The silent float is the perfect opportunity for you to practice being conscious. There will be no conversations to distract you, so you can really look at yourself, this trip, what you have learned, and what you will be doing differently as a result.

"While you are listening and observing the Canyon's wake up time, think back on these past two weeks. What is different about you now because of your Canyon experience? What awareness do you have now that you didn't have when you began this vacation getaway? What did you bring into the Canyon in the form of beliefs, judgments and attitudes that you no longer need? Your silent time is your opportunity to anchor the 'gifts' you have received from the Canyon, as well as a chance to 'give away' those things you no longer need.

"In anticipation of your questions, I'll explain what I mean by 'gifts' and 'giveaways.' A gift is any new awareness that can improve the quality of your life. It could be a new understanding of how you have been that has interfered with you getting what you want in your life. It could be a lesson you received from an experience, like the tyrant's lesson your got through Frank. It could be a new tool, like walking around the wheel to gain a fresh perspective, or the Wheel of Effortless Energy. Anything that provides insight into who you are and what or how to do things differently as a way to enjoy life more.

"A 'giveaway' is any act that consciously lets go of something that is unwanted and doesn't serve you anymore. Remember, death gives life, etc. Something has to die before there can be a rebirth. Nature abhors a vacuum. In giving away your need to judge others, for example, you create space for learning what another may be teaching you. What you judge you hold on to. Since no two things can occupy the same space, any judgment of anything or anybody interferes with your growth in that area.

"So, this morning, when you give away what you no longer need, you will be introducing yourself consciously to a very powerful process that will give you freedom to be who you are. Fill the vacuum you create in your giveaway with the gifts you have received from the Canyon and the people on this trip. Decide what you have learned and, most importantly, how your life is to be different after you leave here.

"This ending ceremony, as I shall call your silent float, has three features. Giveaways, gifts, and what you will do differently. They are all part of the whole. Your giveaways (what you release) and your gifts (what you embrace) will result in a whole new choreography in your life. The choices you will make, the actions you will take, the things you will stop doing as well as begin doing, are great gifts, both to yourself and to those around you. Indeed to the entire world, because as you change your consciousness, you send that new consciousness into the world to improve the consciousness of the world.

"I see that last thought is a difficult one to understand. In time you will gain insight into how all things are connected. There are no random thoughts or actions. All thought, all action has an impact on the whole. I ask you to accept that without question at this time. You have more immediate fish to fry. Don't get distracted by this. Your time here has been meaningful and relatively easy. Your most challenging and important work begins now.

"Are you clear on what you must do this morning, Charly?"

"Yes, very clear. Thank you, Spirit Dancer. Thank you." I was feeling humble and thankful for this explanation and all I had learned from her. "Will I see you again?"

"Of course. Only the time and place are unknown. I wish you well on your journey. There is no time and no space in the world of Spirit, Charly. Good-bye for now, hello forever." With that she blazed another trail across the sky disappearing into the hint of a new day illuminating the Eastern horizon.

I handed my two river bags to Dean who tied them down on the tube behind his cooler. All that remained was the bathroom gear which was being loaded on James' boat. With a silent signal from Greg, we all jumped aboard our respective rafts and shoved off for our last moments on the river. Even with the silence, or perhaps because of it, the emotions of bringing this incredible trip to an end were evident on several faces, including, surprisingly enough, Frank.

He had been so quiet the last few days I had almost forgotten how obnoxious I thought he was early on. Did he change that much, or was the change in me? It was a provocative question to begin my float.

It was light enough to see the river, but we were still at least a half hour away from sunrise. The Canyon is very still at this time of day, with the exception of the river, which has no competition for its voice. I could hear the waves lapping at the sides of Marian's raft, the sound of her oars skimming over the top of the water as she feathered them in a dance between oar blade and the shimmering river. I could also hear my own breathing in the silence of the nascent day.

We ran one final small, but feisty and noisy rapid, and then Marian shipped her oars and we floated the last mile and a half in silence. My list of giveaways, gifts, and how I will be different was long. Most important, I think, was the new awareness I would take back with me. Awareness I owe to Spirit Dancer, my new tribe, and the Grand Canyon. It would require more time than this Dawn Float to take in this massive experience, integrate what Spirit Dancer had taught me, and start applying it in my personal and professional life. I decided the first step I would take when I got back home was to use my first weekend and go to a friend's cabin in Northern Michigan where I would develop a plan to live the life I wanted. I knew the changes would be substantial and challenging.

The Grand Canyon had made an indelible mark on me. I could never again be the same as I was before the trip. I was scared and excited. Scared of all the unknowns, most of which were really "knowns", as I had learned from Jane. Excited that for the first time in my life I knew things could be different and also knew it was up to me to create what I wanted.

As we ended our trip celebration dinner back in Flagstaff that night, Wally's parting words hung in the air like a neon sign. "All who travel through the Grand Canyon come out the other end different, Charly." If he only knew.

Afterword

Many years after this first trip, a shaman said to me, "Charly, you have mastered being in the Canyon, now you can master being in the city." It's one thing to have a powerful experience in some spectacular place away from our normal life, and another to take that experience and use it wisely "back home."

"Back home" is where all the old habits reside. It's where friends, family and working associates are used to certain behaviors ingrained over a lifetime of living according to the picture on the outside of the box. As I found out, changing those habits, beliefs and actions of a lifetime is challenging at best, and requires the strongest possible intention, focus, support, and commitment.

When I returned to Michigan, I was filled with enthusiasm for "the new me," and excited about integrating the things I had learned while in the Canyon. But you know how it is. The job is demanding, nothing and nobody else has changed because of my experience, there's all this "stuff" tugging at my time, attention and energy.

Within a couple of weeks I felt I was right back where I started when I left for my Canyon adventure. One night I received a very brief visit from Spirit Dancer. I was sitting in the dark of my living room feeling trapped and sorry for myself when I saw her in front of me, hands on her hips. Her voice was focused and strong.

"What is your intention, Charly? Are you interested in taking the next step? Or do you want to continue in your current rut? It's not all that bad, after all. You have a decent job, a nice place to live, three squares a day. Could be worse.

"Remember your Dawn Float, Charly? What about that list of gifts and how you would be different? Was that just a throwaway exercise? A way to tease yourself like a petulant child? What's next, my friend? More of the same?"

Then she was gone, and I was left feeling attacked and hopeless. Feeling incapable to do anything about anything, I decided to go to bed, hoping the next day would offer more options.

I woke in the morning with what felt like a hangover. I had spent most of the night tossing and turning unable to let go of Spirit Dancer's pointed questions. What would I do? There was no doubt I was sick and tired of the way things were. But how to make it any different? I didn't think I had any control over the situation. I lay in bed overwhelmed by feelings of fear and sadness. I was afraid that nothing would change, and sad about the memory of my enthusiasm and optimism just a couple of weeks before.

Then I saw my journal, which I hadn't opened since returning from the Canyon. I reached for it and opened it to the last entry listing the gifts and what I committed to changing. As I read through the list, the memory of that determined feeling seeped back. Three changes stood out:

• Take personal responsibility for my choices, accept personal responsibility for my experiences

• I will be an explorer and go where I've never been before to improve the quality of my life and those around me

• I will stop waiting—for the world to come to me, for people to take care of me, for someone to rescue me.

I sat up and reread my journal for the entire trip. When I finished I realized what I needed to do. I picked up the phone and called my friend Bill who had the cabin in Northern Michigan. He was happy to let me use it for a few days, and by noon I was on the road. The five hour journey felt like my drive to Arizona, filled with curiosity and optimism. I didn't know what would happen during my time on Lake Michigan, but somehow I "knew" it would be productive.

I arrived about five o'clock, made sure all my gear was put away, laid out the food I would prepare for dinner, and went for a walk on the beach. It wasn't the Colorado, but just being by the water had a calming effect on me.

I walked for several miles and then sat idly watching the sun sink into the lake. The sky radiated an array of brilliant colors that reminded me of the rock pallet in the Canyon.

"Welcome home, Charly." It was Spirit Dancer, smiling as she floated toward me from out of the setting sun. Her voice was soothing. "Congratulations for taking your life in your hands."

"What do you mean?" I asked, feeling as though I had let her down. "I haven't done anything but slip back into my old rut since I've been back."

"Perhaps you just needed a little more discomfort before you were ready to take a stand. Remember, we learn through pleasure or pain. Looks like you've reached that critical mass of pain where you're willing to face your fears and make some changes.

"Life is a journey, Charly. It's taken all your life to get in the condition you are currently in. Don't expect change to occur overnight."

"But I was so optimistic and certain things would be different when I returned from my trip. That's why I was so disappointed when I slipped back into my old habits. My job demanded so much of my energy, and my friends didn't seem to want to hear what I had learned. They seemed to get nervous when I told them some of the things you taught me."

"As I would expect, Charly," she replied with an understanding smile. "The circumstances of your life are a reflection of your own consciousness. So the people and activities around you mirror who you were before your trip. You are now in transition, my friend, and it's time for you to create your ending ceremony."

"What would that be like, Spirit Dancer?" I asked.

She paused for a moment, making me a little nervous. "For most of your life, Charly, you have not been in relationship with yourself. Instead, like many others who need approval and love, you have been like the chameleon, changing your colors so others would like and include you. Do you want to continue that approach to life?"

"Absolutely not!" I was emphatic.

"Then you must create an ending ceremony, just like we discussed in the Canyon. Only this time, you must be ready to take off that chameleon mask and step forward as who you really are."

"I want to really badly, but I don't see how I can change what I've been doing my whole life. That's why I'm so scared."

"It's a big step for you to acknowledge your fear. But it's not enough. You have to go beyond the emotion and find out what you need. What do you need to move through the fear, Charly?" She was very focused and there was no pity in her voice.

"I don't know, damn it! If I did, I would have done something about it by now." My heart was pounding and my gut felt like it housed a 25 pound bowling ball.

"Okay, I hear your fear and frustration. Try this. Close your eyes and take several deep breaths." I did as she said.

"Good. Now where in your body do you feel stuck?"

"In my gut, it feels like an oversized bowling ball." At least my humor wasn't totally lost.

"Focus on that area of your body where you feel the bowling ball. What is the emotion, mad, sad, glad, or scared?"

At first I didn't trust what she was doing. Oh hell, it wasn't her I didn't trust, it was my ability to listen to my internal communication.

"Don't force it. Just let it emerge."

"Sad," I replied, a little hesitantly, "sad." I felt tears appear out of the corners of my eyes and trace a slow, warm path to the edge of my mouth.

"Okay, that's great." Her manner was very comforting. "Now focus on that area again, and ask it what it needs. What does the sadness want. And don't filter it. Just respond to what you notice."

"I need to feel okay just the way I am and trust I have the answers." I was surprised by the clarity of my words.

"Excellent. You do have the answers, Charly, as you just demonstrated. This is a process you are in, and once you have done your ending ceremony, you will be in the Transition Zone where the only unknown is time.

"Effective change occurs over long periods of time. You have many layers of beliefs and attitudes that are from the picture on the outside of your box. It will take time to identify and replace those that don't serve you.

"Your biggest challenge in the Transition Zone will be to learn to trust yourself, your instincts and choices, the process, Spirit.

You have taken on one of the most important missions in life, and that is to let go of who you are not and step into who you are. It will involve letting go of all your teachings, literally all you know up to this point.

"You are accustomed to the 'nice guy approach' as a way to play it safe and receive approval and attention. Now you must forget the nice and make decisions by being open to the dialogue of what Life is telling you right now. It is the process you must go through of moving toward that which is 'known' to you, and making your decisions from that place. Do you understand?"

"No. It sounds like you are telling me to become selfish. I want to be in a relationship sometime soon, and nobody will want me if they see me as self centered."

"Right now it seems selfish to you, but that is because you don't trust the process. When you learn to live from an internal flow, from a focus on believing in yourself, you will become more available to be in relationship with others, and, in fact, will be much more attractive to powerful people who will seek you out.

"But you're not ready for that yet. You first must come into a powerful relationship with yourself. Learn to do only for you. Your dance is with yourself right now. Make choices and decisions that will keep you in your power. Up until now you have given your power away every time you have wanted something and were afraid you wouldn't get it. This requires a lot of faith, Charly, and requires you to stick to what you know is true while not giving away your power.

"Don't allow yourself to give away your power to anyone, anything, or any idea, not even for one minute. You should be consumed by this task. Continually check in, asking the question, "what do I need now?" As a result you will develop a core so strong you will become self-referent and know what you need to do at any time. Eventually all your actions will come from that understanding.

"You have the inherent ability to know when you are congruent with who you are. When you know where you belong within yourself, then you will be available to dance in a relationship you can only dream of in this moment. Instead of trying to fit yourself in, which is the result of not feeling okay inside, you will know what it feels like to belong. There will be no projecting, no interest in fixing others, and none of the old habit of using others to feed that empty, not-good-enough self you have known in the past.

"I would call it beautiful fierceness. It is like your totem, the red-tailed hawk. There is no doubt that bird is centered, self-referent, very powerful, and beautiful. From that place you can say 'I love you' and it will go directly to the heart, because it comes from your heart. That is where fierce beauty resides. That is where your power will emerge.

"I have said enough. Create your ceremony, Charly. When you have done that, you will have a void to fill. Fill it with yourself, that beautiful, fierce person you really are. You are ready. Fly high my friend, and know I am not separate from you. We will meet again. For now, let's see how good you are willing to make your life. Enjoy your adventure dancing on the edge."

I didn't want her to leave. I wanted her help in creating my ceremony. But I knew it was up to me, and her hawk image was still dancing in my mind. Again I found myself in the dark, a long way from home. But I wasn't concerned. The beach was clear, and I was confident I could find my cabin since it was on a point jutting out into the lake. I would enjoy my star filled walk back to the cabin, prepare a sumptuous meal, get a good night's sleep, and create my ceremony tomorrow. And then? Well, it wouldn't be easy, there would be many challenges. I would be going where I have never been before, but now it was feeling more like an adventure, an exploration. A homecoming. Just like my Canyon trip.

About the Author

Charly Heavenrich is a speaker, writer, and photographer, and has been a Grand Canyon raft guide since 1978. He has an MBA in International Business and Finance and has studied with many powerful teachers in the fields of consulting, self-esteem, Universal Principles, ceremony, spirituality, personal growth, athletics, and environmental awareness. Charly has been an athlete (NCAA baseball championship); a businessman in fields including fitness, construction, insurance, and consulting; and is committed to sharing the adventure of life with those he touches. He is a student of life and considers his life experiences, especially in the Grand Canyon, to be his greatest teachers.

Canyon Discoveries Services

CANYON DISCOVERIES SERVICES offers programs and products from Charly Heavenrich. This includes audiotapes and videotapes; books; speaking and consulting services; one-on-one consultations for individuals and leaders dealing with the challenges of change; Grand Canyon images; and screen savers.

CHARLY HEAVENRICH is available to speak to your group. His programs include:

• **"BEYOND THE EDGE"**—A virtual journey through the Grand Canyon with slides, music, Canyon sounds, and inspiring stories that introduce principles to help you be more effective in your personal and professional lives.

• **"SIMPLE SPLENDOR"**—A compelling audio-visual presentation with slides and music. Ideal for a break in your company's meetings and for public and church groups.

• **"THE POWER OF CONSCIOUS TRANSITION"**—A 3 to 12 hour workshop to provide the tools and strategies for dealing successfully with the rapids of change.

CONTACT:
Charly Heavenrich
P.O. Box 1555
Boulder, CO 80306-1555
(303) 545-5414
email: cheavnrich@aol.com
www.Heavenrich.com

PLEASE SEND ME INFORMATION ON CHARLY'S PRODUCTS AND SERVICES.

Dancing on the Edge $14.95 each plus shipping and handling
(shipping is $3 for first copy and $1 for each additional copy)

Quantity _____ books

Shipping _____

Tax $.45/book _____ (3%, Colorado residents only)

Discount for orders
of 4 or more books _____

Total enclosed $_____

> **10% discount on orders of 4 or more books**

I'd like to learn more about:

_____Books, Audiotapes, and Videotapes

_____Speaking Engagements

_____One-on-One Consultations

_____Canyon Images

_____Screen Savers

_____ ( ) _____
Name   Phone

_____
Street Address or P.O. Box

_____
City   State   Zip

_____
E-mail address

Please mail orders to:
Charly Heavenrich
P.O. Box 1555
Boulder, CO 80306-1555

> **Please make checks payable to Charly Heavenrich**